Robbins collection of
GILBERT &
SULLIVAN
SONGS

Edited and Arranged by
HUGO FREY

PRICE
$3.95

Copyright 1942
ROBBINS MUSIC CORPORATION
NEW YORK, N.Y.

CONTENTS BY TITLES

CONTENTS BY OPERAS

H. M. S. PINAFORE

or THE LASS THAT LOVED A SAILOR

First performed May 25, 1878, at the Opéra Comique, London

THE STORY

Ralph Rackstraw, Able Seaman from H.M.S. Pinafore, loves Josephine, his Captain's daughter. But all hands agree he has no chance, due to his lowly and her exalted station.

Captain Corcoran is also troubled. He is anxious for a match between Josephine and Sir Joseph Porter, First Lord of the Admiralty, who is arriving in the afternoon to claim her hand in marriage. When pressed by her father for a reason why she is so cool to Sir Joseph, she replies that she loves a common sailor.

Sir Joseph arrives with much dignity and fanfare, accompanied by many devoted cousins and aunts. He makes an inspiring speech, explaining to the seamen that they are any man's equal—excluding Sir Joseph. Taking this perhaps too literally, Ralph is emboldened to speak of his love to Josephine, and after the customary expressions of indignation, she accepts him and agrees to elope with him after dark.

That night, while Captain Corcoran is strolling on the poop-deck, he meets Little Buttercup. Finding him sad, she hints of her love for him, and when he replies that the difference in their station prevents his being more than a friend, she enigmatically replies that being of Gypsy blood, she can foresee a great change in store for him. She exits without revealing what the change is to be.

Sir Joseph enters, piqued. His dignity has suffered another rebuff from Josephine. Soothingly, the Captain explains there must surely be only one reason why she refuses so fine and dazzling a fellow—that is, she feels the difference in their rank.

At the first opportunity, therefore, Sir Joseph explains to Josephine that she should allow no considerations of rank to interfere with love. He is so eloquent that he removes her last doubts over her impending elopement with Ralph! She replies, significantly, that she will take his words as an official opinion.

Captain Corcoran, thinking she means to accept the Admiral, is happy until informed by Dick Deadeye, an ugly and envious fellow, of the impending elopement. Furious, the Captain hides by wrapping himself about with his cloak. Josephine, Ralph and the crew, accompanied by Buttercup, tiptoe on deck. The elopement is stopped, and poor Ralph seems certainly doomed to an indefinite sojourn in the ship's dungeon, when Buttercup confounds everyone with an amazing confession.

When she was very young, according to her statement, she was once employed at a baby farm. While there, she nursed two children, one of high, the other of lowly birth. And these two, of course, were Ralph Rackstraw and Captain Corcoran. By some accident, she had mixed the two babies, so really Ralph is the one of high birth and Captain Corcoran is of low birth. So Ralph becomes Captain, and Corcoran is demoted to common seaman.

Thus, the mix-up is happily unscrambled. Ralph is now eligible to marry Josephine, while the erstwhile Captain Corcoran finds consolation with Buttercup. And finally, Sir Joseph's heart and dignity are both saved, for Josephine is much too common for him. He therefore marries Hebe, his first cousin, presumably as protection against his other, and numerous, sisters, cousins and aunts.

WE SAIL THE OCEAN BLUE

Opening Chorus - Sung by the Crew

Words by
W. S. GILBERT

Music by
Sir ARTHUR SULLIVAN

Ports - mouth tide, We've plen - ty of time for play, A - hoy! A -

hoy! The balls whis - tle free A - hoy! A - hoy! O'er the bright blue

sea, We stand to our guns, to our guns all day. _____ We

sail the o - cean blue, And our sau - cy ship's a beau - ty; We're

so - ber men and true, And at - ten - tive to our du - ty; Our

sau - cy ship's a beau - ty, We're at - ten - tive to our

cresc.

du - ty; We're so - ber men and true, We sail the

o - cean blue.

"H. M. S. Pinafore"

I'M CALLED LITTLE BUTTERCUP

Sung by Buttercup

Words by
W. S. GILBERT

Music by
Sir ARTHUR SULLIVAN

Arr. by Hugo Frey

I've snuff and to-bac-cy and ex-cel-lent jack-y; I've scis-sors and watch-es and knives. I've rib-bons and la-ces to set off the fa-ces of pret-ty young sweet-hearts and wives, I've trea-cle and tof-fee, I've tea and I've cof-fee, Soft tom-my and suc-cu-lent chops,

I've chick-ens and co-nies, and pret-ty po-lo-nies, and ex-cel-lent pep-per-mint drops. —— Then buy of your But-ter-cup, Dear lit-tle But-ter-cup, sail-ors should nev-er be shy. —— So buy of your But-ter-cup, poor lit-tle But-ter-cup, Come of your But-ter-cup buy. ——

A MAIDEN FAIR TO SEE

Sung by Ralph

Words by
W. S. GILBERT

Music by
Sir ARTHUR SULLIVAN

ny-ing, Has dared for her to pine, At whose ex-al-ted shrine A world of wealth is

CHORUS

RALPH

sigh-ing. A world of wealth is sigh-ing. Un-learn-ed he in aught Save

that which love has taught, (For love had been his tu-tor;) Oh, pi-ty, pi-ty me Our

CHORUS

cap-tain's daugh-ter, she, And I that low-ly suit-or! Oh, pi-ty, pi-ty me Our

cap-tain's daugh-ter, she, And I that low-ly suit-or.

"H. M. S. Pinafore"

I AM THE CAPTAIN OF THE "PINAFORE"

Sung by Capt. Corcoran

Words by
W. S. GILBERT

Music by
Sir ARTHUR SULLIVAN

Arr. by Hugo Frey

very, ver-y good, and — be it un-der-stood, he com-mands a — right good
ceed-ing-ly po-lite, and he thinks it on-ly right, to re-turn the — com-pli-

(CAPTAIN

crew.   Tho' re-la-ted to a peer, I can   hand reef— and steer, or
ment.   Bad   lan-guage or a-buse, I   nev-er, nev-er use, what

ship— a— sel-va— gee;   I am nev-er known to quail   at the
ev-er the e-mer-gen- cy;   Tho'— "both-er it" I may oc-

CHORUS

fu-ry of the gale And I'm   nev-er, nev-er sick at   sea!   What
ca-sion-al-ly say,   I   nev-er use a big, big,   D!   What

SORRY HER LOT

Sung by Josephine

Words by
W. S. GILBERT

Music by
Sir ARTHUR SULLIVAN

Arr. by Hugo Frey

"H. M. S. Pinafore"

OVER THE BRIGHT BLUE SEA

Sung by the Chorus

Words by
W. S. GILBERT

Music by
Sir ARTHUR SULLIVAN

O - ver the bright blue sea _____ Comes Sir Jo - - seph Por - ter, K. C. B. Wher - ev - - er he may go _____ Bang, bang the loud nine pound - ers go!

I AM THE MONARCH OF THE SEA

Sung by Sir Joseph

Words by
W. S. GILBERT

Music by
Sir ARTHUR SULLIVAN

Arr. by Hugo Frey

an-chor here I ride, My bo-som swells with pride, And I snap my fin-gers at a

HEBE　　　　　　　　　　　　　　　　　　　　　　　　　**CHORUS**

foe-man's taunts. And so do his sis-ters and his cou-sins and his aunts. And

cresc.　　　　　　　　　　　　　**ALL**

so do his sis-ters and his cou-sins and his aunts, His sis-ters and his cou-sins and his

cresc.

SIR JOSEPH

aunts. _____

But when the breez-es blow I

gen-er-al-ly go be-low, And seek the se-clu-sion that a cab-in grants. And

SOPRANOS & ALTOS

so do his sis-ters and his cou-sins and his aunts, And so do his sis-ters and his

ALL *cresc.* *f*

cou-sins and his aunts. And so do his sis-ters and his cou-sins and his aunts, His

cresc. *f sempre*

sis-ters and his cou-sins; Whom he reck-ons up by doz-ens, and his aunts. ____

marcato *fz*

"H. M. S. Pinafore"

WHEN I WAS A LAD

Sung by Sir Joseph

Words by
W. S. GILBERT

Music by
Sir ARTHUR SULLIVAN

1. When I was a lad I served a term As of - fice boy to an At - tor - ney's firm, I cleaned the win-dows and I
2. As of - fice boy I made such a mark That they gave me the post of a jun - ior clerk. I served the writs with a
3. In serv-ing writs I made such a name That an ar - ti - cled clerk I soon be-came; I wore clean col-lars and a
4. Of le-gal knowl-edge I ac - quired such a grip That they took me in to the part - ner - ship, And that jun - ior part - ner -

Arr. by Hugo Frey

CHORUS

swept the floor, And I pol-ished up the han-dle of the big front door. He—
smile so bland, And I cop-ied all the let-ters in a big round hand. He—
bran' new suit For the pass ex-am-in-a-tion at the In-sti-tute. For the
ship I ween Was the on - ly ship— that I ev-er had seen. Was the

SIR JOSEPH

pol-ished up the han-dle of the big front door. I pol-ished up that han-dle so
cop-ied all the let-ters in a big round hand. I cop-ied all the let-ters in a
pass ex-am-in-a-tion at the In - sti-tute. That pass ex-am-in-a-tion did so
on - ly ship— that he ev-er had seen. But that kind of ship so

CHORUS

care-ful-lee, That now I am the rul-er of the Queen's Na-vee! He
hand so free, That now I am the rul-er of the Queen's Na-vee! He
well for me, That now I am the rul-er of the Queen's Na-vee! That
suit-ed me, That now I am the rul-er of the Queen's Na-vee! But

pol-ished up that han-dle so care-ful-lee, That now he is the rul-er of the
cop-ied all the let-ters in a hand so free, That now he is the rul-er of the
pass ex-am-in-a-tion did so well for he, That now he is the rul-er of the
that kind of ship so suit-ed he, That now he is the rul-er of the

Queen's Na-vee.
Queen's Na-vee.
Queen's Na-vee.
Queen's Na-vee.

5. I grew so rich that I was sent
   By a pocket borough into Parliament.
   I always voted at my party's call,
   And I never thought of thinking for myself at all.
   He never thought of thinking for himself at all.
   I thought so little, they rewarded me,
   By making me the ruler of the Queen's Navee.
   He thought so little, they rewarded he,
   By making him the ruler of the Queen's Navee.

6. Now landsmen all, whoever you may be,
   If you want to rise to the top of the tree,
   If your soul isn't fettered to an office stool,
   Be careful to be guided by this golden rule.
   Be careful to be guided by this golden rule.
   Stick close to your desks and never go to sea,
   And you all may be rulers of the Queen's Navee.
   Stick close to your desks and never go to sea,
   And you all may be rulers of the Queen's Navee.

"H. M. S. Pinafore"

REFRAIN, AUDACIOUS TAR

Sung by Josephine and Ralph

Words by
W. S. GILBERT

Music by
Sir ARTHUR SULLIVAN

tar, Re - mem - ber what you are. I'd
way, You speak, and I o - bey. My

Refrain, Poco lento

laugh my rank to scorn In u - nion ho - ly, Were he more high - ly
heart, with an - guish torn, Bows down be - fore her; She laughs my love to

Espressivo

born Or I__ more low - ly. I'd laugh my rank to scorn In u - nion
scorn; Yet I__ a - dore her, My heart, with an - guish torn, Bows down be -

rit.

1. RALPH. 2.

ho - ly, Were he more high - ly born Or I more low - ly. Proud
fore her. She laughs my love to scorn, Yet I a - dore her.

rit.

colla voce

"H. M. S. Pinafore"

Things Are Seldom What They Seem

Sung by Buttercup and the Captain

Words by
W. S. GILBERT

Music by
Sir ARTHUR SULLIVAN

BUTTERCUP

Drops the wind and stops the mill, Tur - bot is am - bi - tious brill;

Gild the far - thing if you will, Yet it is a far - thing still.

CAPTAIN

Yes, I know, That is so. Tho' to catch your drift I'm

striv - ing, It is shad - y it is shad - y;

I don't see at what you're driv-ing, Mys-tic la-dy, mys-tic la-dy.

BOTH

Stern con-vic-tion's o'er {me/him} steal - ing That the mys - tic

la - dy's deal - ing In o-rac - u - lar re - veal - ing.

CAPTAIN

Yes, I know.

BUTTERCUP

That is so!

Never Mind The Why And Wherefore

Sung by Sir Joseph, the Captain and Josephine

Words by
W. S. GILBERT

Music by
Sir ARTHUR SULLIVAN

Nev-er mind   the why and where-fore, Love can lev-el ranks, and there-fore, Though his
Nev-er mind   the why and where-fore, Love can lev-el ranks, and there-fore, Though your
Nev-er mind   the why and where-fore, Love can lev-el ranks, and there-fore I ·ad-

Lord-ship's sta·tion's might·y, Though stu-pen-dous be his brain, Though her
nau-ti-cal re- la-tion In my set could scarce-ly pass, Though you
mit the ju-ris- dic-tion; A- bly have you play'd your part, You have

tastes are mean and flight-y And her for-tune poor___ and plain___
oc- cu-py a sta-tion In the low-er mid - dle class___
car- ried firm con-vic-tion To my hes-i-ta - ting heart___

The Merry Maiden And The Tar

Sung by Deadeye and Capt. Corcoran

Words by
W. S. GILBERT

Music by
Sir ARTHUR SULLIVAN

Allegro

DEADEYE

1. Kind Cap-tain, I've im-por-tant in-for-ma - tion, Sing
fel - low, in con-un-drums you are speak - ing, Sing
Cap - tain, your young la - dy is a - sigh - ing, Sing
fel - low, you have giv-en time-ly warn - ing, Sing

hey, the kind Com - man-der that you are, _____ A -
hey, the mys-tic sail - or that you are, _____ The
hey, the sim - ple Cap - tain that you are, _____ This
hey, the thought-ful sail - or that you are, _____ I'll

bout a cer - tain in-ti-mate re - la - - tion, __ Sing
an - swer to them vain-ly I am seek - - ing, __ Sing
ver - y night with Rack-straw to be fly - - ing, __ Sing
talk to Mas - ter Rack-straw in the morn - - ing, __ Sing

Arr. by Hugo Frey

"H. M. S. Pinafore"

CAREFULLY ON TIPTOE STEALING

Sung by the Chorus

Words by
W. S. GILBERT

Music by
Sir ARTHUR SULLIVAN

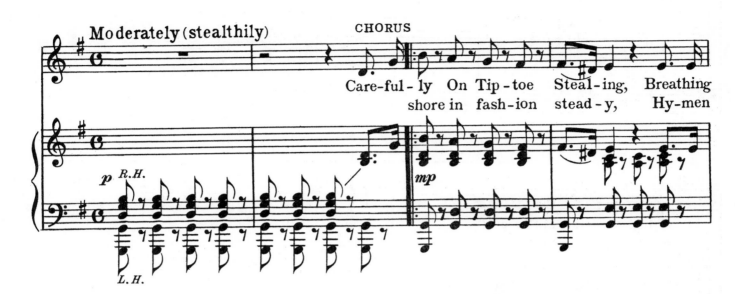

Arr. by Hugo Frey

(CAPTAIN)

be!　　　it was　the cat!　　　It was,　it was　the cat!　They're
be!　　a-gain the cat!　　　It was　a-gain the cat!　They're

right,　　it was the cat!　　　　Pull a-
right,　　it was the　　　　　　cat!　Ev-'ry

step　with cau-tion feel-ing,　We will soft-ly creep a-way,　Ev-'ry

step　with cau-tion feel-ing,　we will steal　a-　way!

FAREWELL MY OWN

Sung by Ralph-Josephine-Sir Joseph-Buttercup and Chorus

Words by
W. S. GILBERT

Music by
Sir ARTHUR SULLIVAN

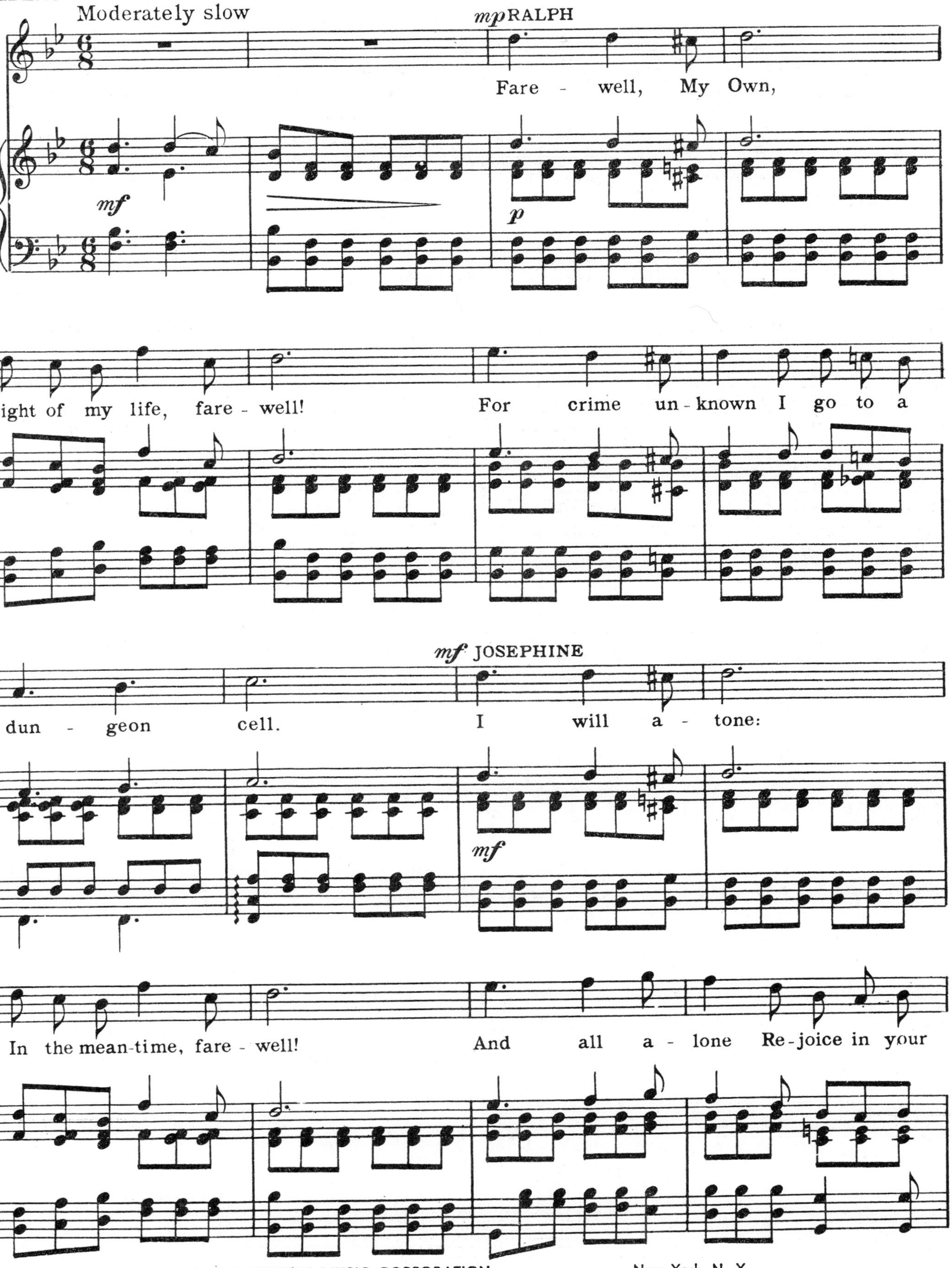

Moderately slow
mp RALPH
Fare - well, My Own,
mf
p
Light of my life, fare - well! For crime un - known I go to a
mf JOSEPHINE
dun - geon cell. I will a - tone:
mf
In the mean-time, fare - well! And all a - lone Re - joice in your

Arr. by Hugo Frey

SIR JOSEPH

dun - geon cell! ___ A bone, ___ a bone ___ I'll

pick with this sail - or fell; ___ Let him be shown At once to his

QUARTET

dun - geon cell. ___ He'll hear no tone ___ Of the

maid - en he loves so well! No tel - e - phone Com - mu - ni - cates with his

LITTLE BUTTERCUP

cell! _____ But when is known_ The se-cret I have to

tell, Wide will be thrown, The door of his dun - geon cell.

f ALL

Fare - well, my own, Light of my life, fare - well! And all a-

lone Re-joice in your dun - geon, your dun - geon cell! _____

For He Loves Little Buttercup

Finale

Words by
W. S. GILBERT

Music by
Sir ARTHUR SULLIVAN

COUSIN HEBE

true to the de -vo -tion that my love im-plants,Then good-bye to your sis -ters, and your

Vivace
CHORUS

cou-sins,and your aunts, Es - pe -cial -ly your cou-sins,Whom you reck-on up by doz-ens. Then good-

bye to your sis -ters, and your cou - sins, and your aunts, Es -

pe - cial -ly your cou - sins, Whom you reck - on up by doz - ens, and your

aunts! For he is an Eng -lish -man! For_

he him-self has said_ it, And it's great-ly

(8va ad lib.)

marcato

(in octaves ad lib.)

to his cred-it, That he is an Eng-lish-

man! That he is __ an __ Eng - - - - - -

- - lish - man!

fff

THE MIKADO

or THE TOWN OF TITIPU

First performed March 14, 1885, at The Savoy, London

THE STORY

Nanki-poo, son of the Mikado of Japan, arrives in Titipu, disguised as a minstrel. He explains to the curious Titiputians that he has come to wed Yum-Yum, with whom he had fallen in love a year before. As she was then betrothed by her guardian, Ko-Ko, Nanki-poo judged his suit hopeless and woefully quit the city.

But, he tells them, he has taken heart once more on learning Ko-Ko has been condemned under the Draconian decree that all who flirt (unless connubially linked) must be beheaded. Nanki-poo thus hopes his rival has been eliminated.

But his hopes are dashed. He learns Ko-Ko has become Lord High Executioner and cannot therefore legally behead anyone until he has cut his own head off. So the wedding, according to Poobah, Lord High Everything else, is to proceed. As Poobah, in his many offices, is to profit from the ceremony, he naturally favors it.

Nanki-poo is consoled to find Yum-Yum does not love Ko-Ko, but to Nanki-poo's suggestion that she throw him over, she replies that he is her guardian and since Titipu girls don't reach the age of discretion until fifty, she is somewhat handicapped in choosing her lovers. And besides, she adds, a ragged minstrel is hardly the match for a ward of the Lord High Executioner.

Nanki-poo then tells her the real reason for his disguise. At court he had the misfortune to capture the affections of Katisha, an elderly and homely lady of the Mikado's court. Having been claimed by the amorous Katisha under the Mikado's law, Nanki-poo could only flee, disguised as a second trombone.

At this point, all of Titipu, especially the Lord High Executioner, are thrown into consternation by a letter from the Mikado complaining of the lack of executions in Titipu and decreeing that unless someone is beheaded within one month, the post of Lord High Executioner will be abolished, and the city reduced to the rank of village.

A victim must be found! Ko-Ko contends he cannot cut his own head off, and suggests, since Poobah has so many offices already, he may as well become Lord High Substitute—an office which Poobah delicately declines.

Nanki-poo is the solution! Unable to marry Yum-Yum, he is about to commit suicide, so Ko-Ko suggests he can save the village by allowing himself to be beheaded Nanki-poo, however, refuses unless he is first allowed to marry Yum-Yum and have her as his wife for one month. His clinching argument is, she will be a widow then anyway, and Ko-Ko can marry her.

Ko-Ko agrees, but just then the scorned Katisha appears to claim her lover, Nanki-poo. About to proclaim Nanki-poo as the Mikado's son, Katisha is drowned out by the chorus, and rushes off in a rage.

Nanki-poo and Yum-Yum are about to wed. But Ko-Ko discovers another statute, which says when a married man is beheaded, his wife is buried alive. So if Nanki-poo goes through with the wedding, he condemns Yum-Yum to death; if not, she must marry Ko-Ko.

Seeing no way out, Nanki-poo again prepares to commit suicide, when word comes that the Mikado is in the city to see if his orders have been carried out. Nanki-poo nobly agrees to be beheaded immediately, but Ko-Ko tearfully admits that he can't behead anyone anyhow. He doesn't know how.

So Ko-Ko and Poobah agree to fake an affidavit that Nanki-poo has been lawfully executed, and Nanki-poo is to vanish. Thus the Mikado will be satisfied. But Nanki-poo insists on taking Yum-Yum with him as his bride. Ko-Ko can do nothing but accept these terms.

The Mikado arrives and Ko-Ko begins the gory, though fictional, recital of the execution of Nanki-poo. But the Mikado interrupts to explain he has come on another matter. He is seeking his son and heir, Nanki-poo. And Nanki-poo, according to the affidavit, is dead! So, apologetically, the Mikado condemns Ko-Ko and Poobah to death for "compassing the death of the heir-apparent".

Ko-Ko wants to offer the live body of Nanki-poo as evidence the lad was not beheaded after all, but Nanki-poo refuses to face the furious Katisha, preferring to remain legally dead. The only solution is for Ko-Ko to take her off Nanki-poo's hands. So Ko-Ko, though reluctantly, is forced to woo and win Katisha. Then Nanki-poo reappears with his bride, Yum-Yum.

A WAND'RING MINSTREL I

Sung by Nanki-Poo

Words by
W. S. GILBERT

Music by
Sir **ARTHUR SULLIVAN**

Arr. by Hugo Frey

Behold The Lord High Executioner!

Sung by Ko-Ko and Chorus

Words by
W. S. GILBERT

Music by
Sir ARTHUR SULLIVAN

Allegro marziale

CHORUS

Be-hold the Lord High Ex-e - cu-tion-er! A

per-son-age of no-ble rank and ti - tle A dig-ni-fied and po-tent

of - fi - cer, Whose func - tions are par - tic - u - lar - ly vi - tal! De-

fer,_____ de - fer,_____ To the Lord High Ex - e - cu - tion - er! De-

fer, _____ de - fer, _____ To the no - ble Lord, to the no - ble Lord, to the Lord High __ Ex - e - cu - tion - er!

Fine

Moderato

KO-KO

Tak - en from the coun - ty jail By a set of cu - rious chanc - es, Lib - er - at - ed then on bail, On my own re - cog - ni - zan - ces; Waft - ed by a fav - 'ring gale As one some - times is in

52

"The Mikado"

I'VE GOT A LITTLE LIST

Sung by Ko-Ko and Chorus

Words by
W. S. GILBERT

Music by
Sir ARTHUR SULLIVAN

Allegretto

As

some day it may hap-pen that a vic-tim must be found, I've got a lit-tle list I've
nig-ger ser - e - nad - er, and the oth-ers of his race, And the pia-no or-gan-ist I've
Ni - si Pri - us nuis-ance, who just now is rath-er rife, The Ju - di-cial hu-mor-ist I've

got a lit-tle list Of so - ci - e - ty of-fend-ers who might well be un-der-ground, And who
got him on the list! And the peo-ple who eat pep-per-mint and puff it in your face, They
got him on the list! All fun - ny fel-lows, com-ic men, and clowns of pri-vate life They'd

Arr. by Hugo Frey

"The Mikado"

Three Little Maids From School

Sung by Yum-Yum, Peep-Bo and Pitti-Sing

Words by
W. S. GILBERT

Music by
Sir ARTHUR SULLIVAN

Freed from its ge-nius tu-te-la-ry Three lit-tle maids from

school, Three lit-tle maids ___ from school.

YUM-YUM
One lit-tle maid is a bride, Yum-Yum

PEEP-BO
Two lit-tle maids in at-ten-dance come

Three lit-tle maids who, all un-wa-ry, Come from a la-dies' se-mi-na-ry,

Freed from its ge-nius tu-te-la-ry Three lit-tle maids from

school, Three lit-tle maids ___ from school!

"The Mikado"

Were You Not To Ko-Ko Plighted

Sung by Yum-Yum and Nanki-Poo

Words by
W. S. GILBERT

Music by
Sir ARTHUR SULLIVAN

Arr. by Hugo Frey

"The Mikado"
HE'S GOING TO MARRY YUM-YUM
Sung by Pitti-Sing and Chorus

Words by
W. S. GILBERT

Music by
Sir ARTHUR SULLIVAN

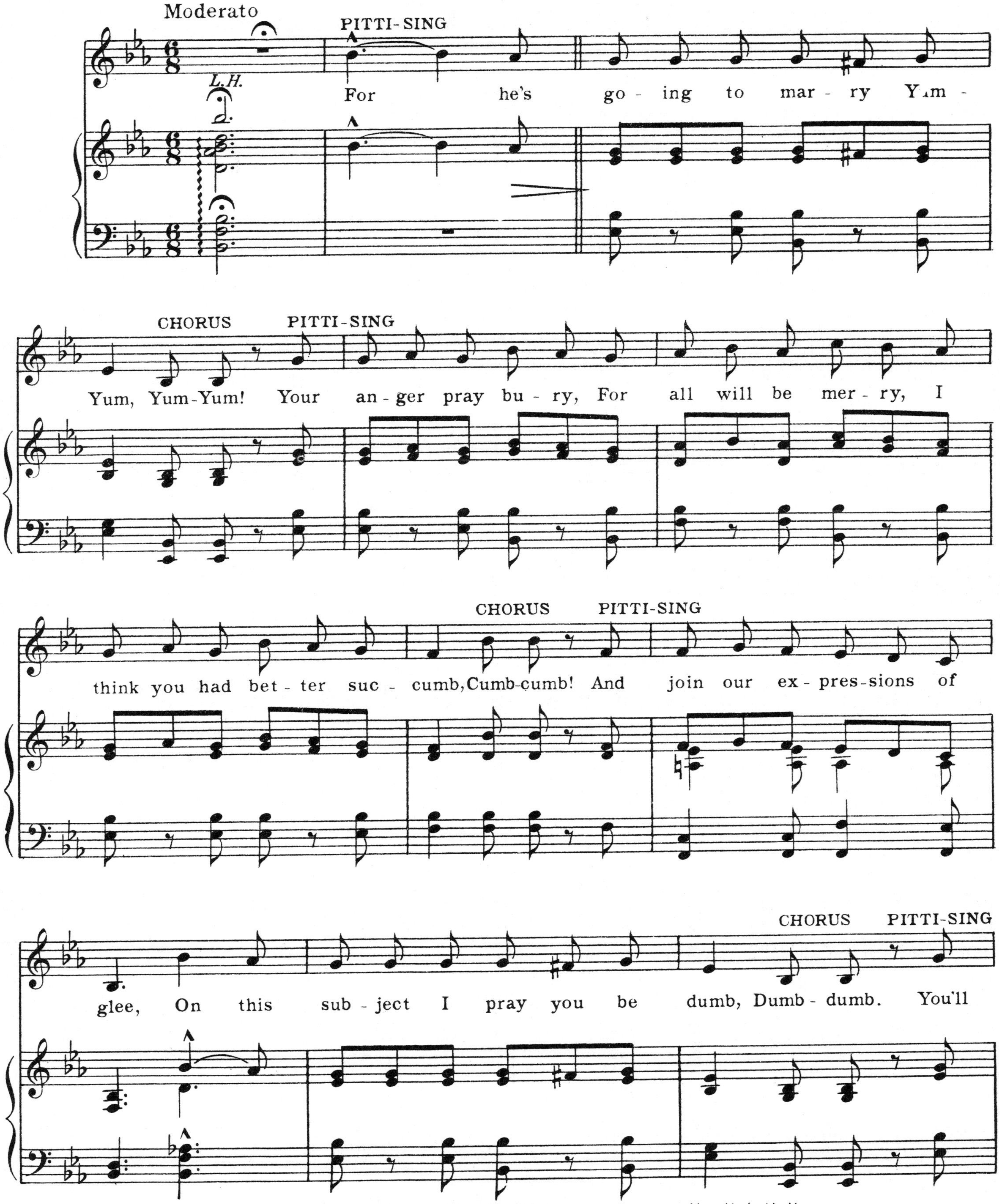

For he's go-ing to mar-ry Yum-Yum, Yum-Yum! Your an-ger pray bu-ry, For all will be mer-ry, I think you had bet-ter suc-cumb, Cumb-cumb! And join our ex-pres-sions of glee, On this sub-ject I pray you be dumb, Dumb-dumb. You'll

find there are man - y Who'll wed for a pen - ny The word for your guid-ance is,

CHORUS   PITTI-SING

"Mum," Mum - mum! There's lots of good fish in the sea! On this

sub - ject we pray you be dumb-dumb-dumb. We think you had bet - ter suc -

cumb - cumb - cumb! You'll find there_ are man - y Who'll wed for a

"The Mikado"

BRAID THE RAVEN HAIR

Sung by the Chorus

Words by
W. S. GILBERT

Music by
Sir ARTHUR SULLIVAN

Braid the ra-ven hair__ Weave the sup - -ple tress__ Deck the maid-en fair__ In her love- -li ness Paint the pret-ty face Dye the cor - al lip Em-pha-size the grace Of her

la - dy - ship! Art and na - ture,

thus— al - lied,—— Go to make a pret - ty

bride! Art and na - ture, thus al - lied, Go to make— a——

pret - ty bride!

THE MOON AND I

Sung by Yum-Yum

Words by
W. S. GILBERT

Music by
Sir ARTHUR SULLIVAN

Andante con modo

The sun, whose rays Are all a-blaze With ev-er-liv-ing glo-ry,
Ob-serve his flame, That pla-cid dame, The moon's Ce-les-tial High-ness;

Does not de-ny His ma-jes-ty He scorns to tell a sto-ry!
There's not a trace Up-on her face Of dif-fi-dence or shy-ness:

He don't ex-claim "I blush for shame, So kind-ly be in-dul-gent"
She bor-rows light That, thro' the night, Man-kind may all ac-claim her!

Arr. by Hugo Frey

"The Mikado"

Brightly Dawns Our Wedding Day

Madrigal

Sung by Yum-Yum, Pitti-Sing, Nanki-Poo and Pish-Tush

Words by
W. S. GILBERT

Music by
Sir ARTHUR SULLIVAN

Arr. by Hugo Frey

73

HERE'S A HOW-DE-DO!

Sung by Yum-Yum, Nanki-Poo and Ko-Ko

Words by
W. S. GILBERT

Music by
Sir **ARTHUR SULLIVAN**

Arr. by Hugo Frey

mess! In a month, or less, I must die with-out a wed-ding! Let the bit-ter

tears I'm shed-ding Wit-ness my dis-tress, Here's a pret-ty mess! Here's a pret-ty

mess!

KO-KO

Here's a state of things! To her life she clings!

Mat-ri-mo-ni-al de-vo-tion Does-n't seem to suit her no-tion Bur-i-al it brings!

KO-KO

ALL

Here's a state of things! Here's a state of things! With a

pas-sion that's in-tense I wor-ship and— a— dore, But the laws of com-mon-

sense We ought-n't to— ig - nore. If what he says is true, 'Tis death to mar-ry

you! Here's a pret-ty state of things! Here's a pret-ty how-de-do! Here's a pret-ty

state of things! a pret-ty state of things! Here's a how-de-do!

KO-KO

Here's a how-de-do! For if what he says is true, I can-not, can-not

mar-ry you! Here's a pret-ty, pret-ty state of things!

Spoken

Here's a pret-ty how-de-do!

MI - YA SA - MA

Sung by the Chorus

Words by
W. S. GILBERT

Music by
Sir ARTHUR SULLIVAN

Mi-ya sa-ma, mi-ya sa-ma, On n'm-ma no ma-yé ni Pi-ra Pi-ra su-ru no wa

Nan gia na To-ko ton-ya-ré ton-ya-ré na!

Arr. by Hugo Frey

"The Mikado"

MY OBJECT ALL SUBLIME

Sung by the Mikado and Chorus

Words by
W. S. GILBERT

Music by
Sir ARTHUR SULLIVAN

"The Mikado"

THE CRIMINAL CRIED

Sung by Pitti-Sing, Ko-Ko, Pooh-Bah and Chorus

Words by
W. S. GILBERT

Music by
Sir ARTHUR SULLIVAN

Ko-Ko The crim-i-nal cried, as he dropp'd him down, In a
Pitti-Sing He shiv-er'd and shook as he gave the sign For the
Pooh-Bah Now tho' you'd have said that head was dead (For its

state of wild a-larm With a fright ful, fran-tic,
stroke he did-n't de-serve;— When all of a sud-den his
own-er dead was he),— It stood on its neck, with a

fear-ful frown, I bar'd my big right arm.— I
eye met mine, And it seem'd to brace his nerve;— For he
smile well bred, And bow'd three times to me! — It was

seiz'd him by his lit-tle pig-tail, And on his knees fell
nod-ded his head and kiss'd his hand, And he whis-tled an air,— did
none of your im-pu-dent off-hand nods, But as hum-ble as could

Arr. by Hugo Frey

he, ___ As he squirm'd and strug-gled, And gur-gled and gug-gled, I
he, ___ As the sa-bre true Cut clean-ly through His
be, ___ For it clear-ly knew The de-fer-ence due To a

drew my snick-er-snee, ___ my snick-er-snee! Oh,
cer-vi-cal ver-te-brae, ___ his ver-te-brae! When a
man of ped-i-gree, ___ of ped-i-gree! And it's

ne'er shall I for-get the cry, Or the shriek that shriek-ed he, ___ As I
man's a-fraid, A beau-ti-ful maid Is a cheer-ing sight to see; ___ And it's
oh, I vow, This death-ly bow Was a touch-ing sight to see; ___ Though

CHORUS

gnash'd my teeth, When from its sheath I drew my snick-er-snee! ___ We
oh, ___ I'm glad That mo-ment sad Was sooth'd by sight of me! ___ Her
trunk-less, yet It could-n't for-get The de-fer-ence due to me! ___ This

know him well, He can-not tell Un-true or ground-less tales___ He
ter-ri-ble tale You can't as-sail, With truth it quite a-grees;___ Her
haugh-ty youth, He speaks the truth When-ev-er he finds it pays;___ And

al-ways tries To ut-ter lies, And ev-'ry time he
taste ex-act For fault-less fact A-mounts to a dis-
in this case It all took place Ex-act-ly as he

1.-2.
fails.___
3.
ease.
says! Ex-act-ly, ex-act-ly, ex-act-ly, ex-

D.C. *ff*

act-ly as he says!___

The Flowers That Bloom In The Spring

Sung by Nanki-Poo and Ko-ko

Words by
W. S. GILBERT
From The Opera "The Mikado"

Music by
Sir ARTHUR SULLIVAN

Brightly

Lyrics (verse 1 / verse 2):

The Flow-ers That Bloom In The Spring, Tra-la, Breathe
The Flow-ers That Bloom In The Spring, Tra-la, Have

pro-mise of mer-ry sun-shine, As we mer-ri-ly dance and we
noth-ing to do with the case, I've got to take un-der my

sing, Tra-la, We wel-come the hopes that they bring, Tra-la, Of a
wing, Tra-la, A most un-at-trac-tive old thing, Tra-la, With a

sum-mer of ro-ses and wine; Of a sum-mer of ro-ses and
ca-ri-ca-ture of a face; With a ca-ri-ca-ture of a

Arr. by Hugo Frey

"The Mikado"

THE LIVING I!

Sung by Katisha

Words by
W. S. GILBERT

Music by
Sir ARTHUR SULLIVAN

Andante moderato

Hearts do not break! They sting and ache For old — love's sake, But do not die! Though with each breath They long for death, As wit - ness - eth The liv - ing I! the liv - ing I! Oh, liv - ing I! Come, tell — me — why, When

Arr. by Hugo Frey

hope is gone, Dost thou stay on?___ Why lin-ger here, Where all is drear?

Oh, liv - ing I! Come, tell___ me___ why, When

hope___ is gone, Dost thou stay on? May not a cheat - ed maid - en

die? May not ___ a cheat - ed maid - en die?

"The Mikado"

TIT WILLOW

Sung by Ko-ko

Words by
W. S. GILBERT
From the Opera "The Mikado"

Music by
Sir ARTHUR SULLIVAN

Copyright 1942 **ROBBINS MUSIC CORPORATION,** New York, N. Y.
International Copyright Secured
Made in U. S. A.

THERE IS BEAUTY

Sung by Katisha and Ko-Ko

Words by
W. S. GILBERT

Music by
Sir ARTHUR SULLIVAN

Arr. by Hugo Frey

WITH JOYOUS SHOUT

Finale

Words by
W. S. GILBERT

Music by
Sir ARTHUR SULLIVAN

Allegro con brio

With joy-ous shout, With joy-ous shout and ring-ing

cheer, In - au - gu - rate, in - au - gu - rate their new ca-

reer! With joy - ous shout and ring - ing

Arr. by Hugo Frey

THE GONDOLIERS

or THE KING OF BARATARIA

First performed December 7, 1889, at The Savoy, London

THE STORY

In Venice lived two gondoliers, friends, who'd "led the last revolution", and who held "that all men are created equal"! The two are loved by all the ladies, so, to be impartial, they decide to choose brides in a game of blindman's buff. Each wins the girl he wanted. As they are starting out to be married, a gondola brings the destitute Duke of Plaza-Toro, from Spain, his Duchess, his daughter Casilda, and the Duke's "suite", consisting of one man, a drummer, Luiz, secretly loved by Casilda.

The Duke reveals to his daughter that, 20 years ago, when she was six months old, she was married by proxy to the baby son of the wealthy King of Barataria, who was kidnapped by the Grand Inquisitor. The Duke has come to search for the heir, and to make Casilda his Queen publicly, as she is in fact. Casilda says, "Queen? But I've nothing to wear!" The Duke explains he has arranged to obtain money by incorporating himself as The Duke of Plaza-Toro, Limited. Casilda, therefore, tells Luiz that "she belongs to another", and repeats her father's explanation.

The Grand Inquisitor tells how he stole the prince. He placed him in the home of a gondolier, who had a baby son of the same age. The gondolier died of drink, and now no one knows which is the prince.

The two gondoliers and their brides return. The Grand Inquisitor, sure that one, he can't guess which, is royal, induces them to come to Barataria, desert their brides for a bit, and rule jointly, until he can find the King's nurse, Inez, who alone can tell which of the two is king. The nurse happens to have been Luiz's mother.

The gondoliers make one condition—they insist on a truly democratic court, in which, according to their long-held ideal, all men shall be equal. Promised this, they take over the kindgom.

In Barataria, the two gondoliers, Giuseppe and Marco, are seated on two thrones, and are themselves cleaning the scepter and crown. Their servants and courtiers are playing cards, shooting dice, etc. Just as the two Kings are lamenting the absence of their wives, the two brides appear. They have arrived, they explain, to mend their socks. They ask, "Which of us is Queen?", and one of the Kings answers that they'll know only when the nurse, Inez, appears. The banquet welcoming the wives is interrupted by the Grand Inquisitor, who is shocked when the Kings tell him that all are equal in rank at Court, even Luiz, the drummer. The Inquisitor announces that which ever of the two is King, will have to marry Casilda.

The Kings and their real brides are desolated by this dilemma of two men married to three women. The two brides sympathize with Casilda, in her vague position. The Duke, who is also shocked at the equality of servants and Kings, tells his daughter to receive her husband properly. She asks, "Which is he?" She says, anyway, she is in love with somebody else. The Kings retort, so are they.

Inez, the nurse, is found, and confesses she substituted her own son for the King, and that Luiz, believed to be her son, is the rightful King.

All are happy. The gondoliers return with their brides to live where all are equal. The Duke's daughter is told she must marry Luiz. She and Luiz rush into each others' arms.

"The Gondoliers"

WE'RE CALLED GONDOLIERI

Sung by Marco and Giuseppe

Words by
W. S. GILBERT

Music by
Sir ARTHUR SULLIVAN

1. We're called _____ gon - do - lier - i, But that's a va -
2. gal - lant - ry not - ed Since we were short -

ga - ry,_ It's_ quite hon - or - a - ry_ The_ trade that_ we_
coat - ed,_ To_ beau - ty_ de - vot - ed_ Giu - sep - pe_ and_

Arr. by Hugo Frey

ply.
I!

2. For
3. When

morn-ing is break-ing, Our couch-es for-sak-ing, To greet their a-

wak-ing With car-ols we come. At sum-mer day's noon-ing, When wea-ry la-

la,   Tra la la la la la la!   Gon - do -

lier - i,   gon - do - lier - i,   Tra   la la la   la, Tra la la la

simile

la, Tra la la la   la, Tra la la la   la, Tra la la la la!

Tra _____   la! _____

IN ENTERPRISE OF MARTIAL KIND

Sung by the Duke

Words by
W. S. GILBERT

Music by
Sir ARTHUR SULLIVAN

Moderato

1. In en-ter-prise of mar-tial kind, When there was an-y fight-ing, He led his reg-i-ment from be-hind He found it less ex-cit-ing. But when a-way his reg-i-ment ran, His place was at the
2. to e-vade De-struc-tion's hand, To hide they all pro-ceed-ed, No sol-dier in that gal-lant band Hid half as well as he did. He lay con-ceal'd through-out the war, And so pre-serv'd his
3. told that they would all be shot Un-less they left the ser-vice, That he ro hes-i-tat-ed not, So mar-vel-lous his nerve is. He sent his res-ig-na-tion in, The first of all his

Arr. by Hugo Frey

"The Gondoliers"

THERE WAS A TIME

Sung by Casilda and Luiz

Words by
W. S. GILBERT

Music by
Sir ARTHUR SULLIVAN

Arr. by Hugo Frey

life, one soul, One aim, one goal.
fade and die, When hope was high.

Each in the oth-er's thrall, Each all in all, ah, woe is
Dead and as far a - way As yes-ter - day, ah, woe is

me! ah woe is me!)
me! ah woe is me!)

calmly

BOTH

Oh bur-y, bur-y let the

mf

grave close o'er, The days that were, that nev - er will be more! Oh

I STOLE THE PRINCE

Sung by Don Alhambra

Words by
W. S. GILBERT

Music by
Sir ARTHUR SULLIVAN

Allegretto non troppo vivo

1. I stole the Prince, and I brought him here, And left him gai - ly pratt - ling With a high - ly res - pect - a - ble gon - do - lier, Who prom - ised the Roy - al babe to rear, And teach him the trade of a ti - mo - neer With his own be - lov - ed

2. ow - ing I'm much dis - posed to fear, To his ter - ri - ble taste for tip - pling, That high - ly res - pect - a - ble gon - do - lier Could nev - er de - clare with a mind sin - cere Which of the two was his off - spring dear, And which the Roy - al

3. sped, and when at the end of a year, I sought that in - fant cher - ished, That high - ly res - pect - a - ble gon - do - lier Was ly - ing a corpse on his hum - ble bier I dropp'd a Grand In - quis - i - tor's tear That gon - do - lier had

4. chil - dren followed his old ca - reer (This state - ment can't be par - ried) Of a high - ly res - pect - a - ble gon - do - lier: Well, one of the two who will soon be here) But which of the two it is not quite clear Is the Roy - al Prince you

108

"The Gondoliers"

WHEN MERRY MAIDEN MARRIES

Sung by Tessa

Words by
W. S. GILBERT

Music by
Sir ARTHUR SULLIVAN

Allegretto grazioso

1. When a mer-ry maid-en mar-ries,
2. When a mer-ry maid-en mar-ries,

Sor-row goes and pleas-ure tar-ries; Ev-'ry sound be-comes a song, All is

Sor-row goes and pleas-ure tar-ries; Ev-'ry sound be-comes a song, All is

right and noth-ing's wrong! From to-day and ev-er af-ter

right and noth-ing's wrong! Gnaw-ing Care and ach-ing Sor-row

Let our tears be tears of laugh-ter, Ev-'ry sigh that finds a vent Be a

Get ye gone un-til to-mor-row; Jeal-ous-ies in grim ar-ray, Ye are

sigh of sweet con - tent! When you mar - ry mer - ry maid - en,
things of yes - ter - day! When you mar - ry mer - ry maid - en;

rit   *a tempo sostenuto*

Then the air with love is lad - en; Ev - 'ry flow'r is a rose, Ev - 'ry
Then the air with joy is lad - en; All the cor-ners of the earth Ring with

goose be - comes a swan, Ev - 'ry kind of trou - ble goes Where the
mu - sic sweet - ly played, Wor-ry is me - lo - dious mirth, Grief is

last year's snows have gone! Sun-light takes the place of shade
joy in - mas - que - rade; Sul - len night is laugh-ing day

CHORUS

When you mar-ry mer-ry maid!_____ When a mer-ry maid-en mar-ries,
All the year is mer-ry May!_____ All the year is mer-ry May,_____

1. Sor-row goes and pleas-ure tar-ries; Ev-'ry sound be-comes a song, All is

right and noth-ing's wrong! **2.** All the year is mer-ry May!__

Mer-ry, mer-ry May, mer-ry, mer-ry May, All the year__ is__ mer-ry, mer-ry May!

"The Gondoliers"

THEN ONE OF US WILL BE QUEEN

Sung by Gianetta and Marco

Words by
W. S. GILBERT

Music by
Sir ARTHUR SULLIVAN

(Gianetta) Then one of us will be a Queen, And
(Marco) drive a-bout in a carriage and pair, With the

sit on a gold-en throne, With a crown in-stead Of a hat on her head, And
King on her left-hand side, And a milk-white horse, As a mat-ter of course, When

di-a-monds all her own! With a beau-ti-ful robe of gold and green, I've
ev-er she wants to ride! With beau-ti-ful sil-ver shoes to wear Up-

al-ways un-der-stood; I won-der wheth-er She'd wear a feath-er? I
on_ her dain-ty feet; With end-less stocks Of beau-ti-ful frocks, And as

rath - er think she should! Oh, — 'tis a glo - ri - ous thing, I ween, To be a
much as she wants to eat!

reg - u - lar Roy - al Queen! No half - and - half af fair, I mean, No

half - and - half af - fair, But a — right-down reg - u - lar, reg - u - lar, reg - u - lar,

1.
reg - u - lar Roy - al Queen!

2.
(*Marco*) She'll Queen!

DANCE A CACHUCHA

Sung by the Chorus

Words by
W. S. GILBERT

Music by
Sir ARTHUR SULLIVAN

Tempo di Cachucha

Dance a_ ca chu- cha, fan- dan- go, bo- le- ro, Xe- res_ we'll

drink Man- za- nil- la, Mon- te_ - ro Wine, when_ it_ runs in a-

Arr. by Hugo Frey

clat-ter Pit-ter, pit-ter, pit-ter, pat-ter, pat-ter, pat-ter, pat-ter, We'll dance, Old

Xe-res we'll drink Man-za-nil-la, Mon-te-ro; For wine, when it runs in a-

bun-dance, en-hanc-es The reck-less de-light of that wild-est of

danc-es, that wild-est of danc-es, The reck-less de-light!

Dance a — ca — chu — cha, fan — dan — go, bo — le — ro, Xe — res — we'll —

drink Man — za — nil — la Mon — te — ro Wine, when — it — runs in a

bun — dance, en — hanc — es The reck — less de — light of that wild — est of danc

es! Old Xe — res we'll drink Man — za — nil — la, Mon —

te - ro, For wine, when it runs in a - bun - dance,   en -

hanc - es The reck - less de - light of that wild - est of danc - es, The

reck - less de - light of that wild - est of danc - -

- - es!

"The Gondoliers"

THERE LIVED A KING

Sung by Don Alhambra, Marco and Giuseppe

Words by
W. S. GILBERT

Music by
Sir ARTHUR SULLIVAN

DON ALHAMBRA

Allegro non troppo

1. There lived a King, as I've been told, In the won-der-work-ing days of old, When Bish-ops_ in their shov-el hats Were hearts were twice as good as gold, And twen-ty times_ as_ mel-low. Good- tem-per tri-umphed in_ his_ face, And in his heart he found a_ place For

2. Chan-cel-lors were cheap as sprats, And plen-ti-ful as tab-by cats In point of fact,_ too_ man-y. Am- bas-sa-dors cropped up_ like_ hay, Prime Min-is-ters and such as_ they Grew

3. King, al-though no one de-nies His heart was_ of ab-nor-mal size, Yet he'd have act-ed oth-er-wise If he had been a_ cu-ter. The end is eas-i-ly_ fore-told, When ev-'ry bless-ed thing you_ hold Is

Arr. by Hugo Frey

"The Gondoliers"

I AM A COURTIER GRAVE

Sung by the Duke, Duchess, Casilda, Marco and Giuseppe

Words by
W. S. GILBERT

Music by
Sir ARTHUR SULLIVAN

an-y-thing, too un-bend-ing Too ag-gres-sive-ly_ stiff and grand; Now to the
twice-ly once-ly, twice-ly Bow im-pres-sive-ly_ ere you glide.

CASILDA

oth-er ex-treme you're tend-ing Don't be so deuc-ed-ly con-de-scend-ing! Now to the

oth-er ex-treme you're tend-ing Don't be so dread-ful-ly con - de - scend-ing!

MARCO

Oh, hard to please some no-ble-men seem! At first, if an-y-thing, too un-

bend-ing; Off_ we_ go to the oth-er ex - treme Too_ con - found-ed-ly_ con-de-

1. scend-ing.

DUKE **2.** 2. Now_ a ga- scend-ing. Cap-i-tal, both,

cap-i-tal, both you've caught it nice-ly! That is the style of_ thing pre - cise-ly! That is the

style of thing, the_ style _____ of thing_ pre - cise - ly!

rit

"The Gondoliers"

ONCE MORE GONDOLIERI

Finale

Words by
W. S. GILBERT

Music by
Sir ARTHUR SULLIVAN

Allegro con brio

Once more _____ gon-do-lier-i, Both skill-ful and wa-ry,— Free_ from this_ quan-da-ry,— Con-tent-ed_ are_ we.____ Ah,—

Arr. by Hugo Frey

From Roy - al - ty fly - ing, Our gon-do-las ply-ing, And

mer - ri - ly_ cry - ing_ Our_ "pre - mé," "sta - li!"_ Ah!_

So

good-bye, ca - chu - cha, fan - dan - go, bo - le - ro We'll dance a fare -

marcato

well to that mea - sure _____ Old Xe - res, a - dieu Man - za -

nil - la Mon - te - ro We leave you with feel - ings of plea - sure!

Once more _____ gon - do - lier - i Both skill - ful and

wa - ry_ Free from this_ quan - da - ry_ Con - tent - ed_ are_ we _____ Ah! _____

Ah!

Once more,_____ gon - do - lier - i,____ gon - do - lier - i,____

— gon - do - lier — — i, Con - tent - ed are we!

So good-bye, ca - chu - cha, fan - dan - go, bo - le - ro We'll

PATIENCE

or BUNTHORNE'S BRIDE

First performed April 23, 1881, at the Opéra Comique, London

THE STORY

"Twenty love-sick maidens" are serenading the aloof, indifferent, long-haired poet and aesthete, Bunthorne. Only one of them, Lady Jane, knows that he is really in love with Patience, the Milkmaid.

The Dragoon Guards, strong, husky and handsome in their uniforms, march in, are annoyed at the maidens' paying court to Bunthorne, and remind them that a year ago they were all engaged to them, the Dragoons. The girls reply, "Bunthorne idealized us." The Colonel and his Dragoons watch Bunthorne pretending to compose a poem, spurning the clinging ladies. The Colonel declares that when he first put his uniform on, he thought no lady could resist him.

Bunthorne, alone, admits that his aestheticism is only assumed to lure the ladies. He sincerely woos Patience but, to his amazement, she refuses him. The ladies tell Patience love is a duty, and it must be unselfish, so she decides to fall in love. Grosvenor, a rival poet to Bunthorne, reminds Patience that he is the little boy she loved when they were children, and that she is attracted to him, but feels it would be selfish to marry a man so perfect as she thinks Grosvenor; she feels she ought to marry Bunthorne, so obviously imperfect.

Bunthorne decides to raffle himself off and sells tickets to the maidens, but just as the raffle is about to begin, Patience announces that she will marry Bunthorne. Upon hearing this, the maidens all become engaged again to their Dragoons, who have copied Bunthorne in his affected attitudes. All leave Bunthorne except Lady Jane.

When Grosvenor appears, the maidens follow after him again, but he still loves Patience and tells them so. Patience is unhappy because, though she loves Grosvenor still, she thinks it her duty to marry Bunthorne, since love must be unselfish.

The rival poets, Bunthorne and Grosvenor, are jealous and hate each other. Bunthorne orders Grosvenor to stop being an aesthete and, at last, Grosvenor promises to do so. Bunthorne, in his triumph over his rival, resolves to be a reformed man, but Patience, at this, breaks with him as there would be nothing unselfish in marrying such a perfect person while Grosvenor, true to his promise, is not an aesthete at all now, but a "commonplace young man", perfectly suitable for her to marry. She promises to wed Grosvenor.

Bunthorne, deserted by Patience, decides to marry Jane, but she marries the Dragoons' friend, the Duke, and as all the maidens are happily paired, the rest of them to the Dragoons, nobody becomes Bunthorne's bride at all, and he is left forlorn.

I CANNOT TELL

Sung by Patience

Words by
W. S. GILBERT

Music by
Sir ARTHUR SULLIVAN

Bright and gracefully

I Can-not Tell what this love may be, that com-eth to
If love is a thorn they show no wit, who fool-ish-ly

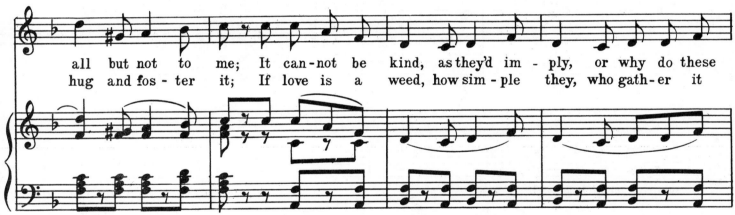

all but not to me; It can-not be kind, as they'd im-ply, or why do these
hug and fos-ter it; If love is a weed, how sim-ple they, who gath-er it

la - dies sigh? I can-not be joy and rap-ture deep, or why do these
day by day! If love is a net-tle that makes you smart, Then why do you

Arr. by Hugo Frey

For I— am blithe and I am gay, while they— sit sigh-ing— night— and day; For I— am blithe and I— am gay Think of the gulf twixt them— and me, Think of the gulf— twixt them— and me, Fa la la la la la la la la la la la la la la_____ and mis - er-y!_____

"Patience"

IF YOU WANT A RECEIPT

Sung by Colonel Fairfax and Chorus

Words by
W. S. GILBERT

Music by
Sir ARTHUR SULLIVAN

Arr. by Hugo Frey

pluck of Lord Nel - son on board of the Vic - to - ry Ge - nius of Bis-mark de -
want a re - ceipt for this sol - dier - like par - a - gon, Get at the wealth of the

vis - ing a plan The hu - mour of Field - ing, (which sounds con - tra - dic - to - ry)
Czar (if you can) The fam - i - ly pride of a Span - iard from Ar - ra - gon

Cool - ness of Pa - get a - bout to tre - pan The sci - ence of Jul - lien, the
Force of Meph - is - to pro - nounc - ing a ban A smack of Lord Wa - ter - ford,

em - i - nent mu - si - co Wit of Mac-au-lay, who wrote of Queen Anne The pa-thos of Pad - dy, as
reck-less and rol - lick - y Swag-ger of Ro-der-ick, head-ing his clan The keen pen - e - tra-tion of

ren-dered by Bou-ci-cault Style of the Bish-op of　So-dor and Man The　dash of a D'Or-say, di-

Pad-ding-ton Pol-la - ky Grace of an O - da-lisque on a di - van The ge-nius stra - te - gic of

vest - ed of quack-er - y Nar - ra - tive pow-ers of　Dick - ens and Thack-er - ay

Cae - sar or Han - i - bal Skill of Sir Gar-net in　thrash - ing a can - ni - bal

Vic-tor Em-man-u - el peak-haunt-ing Pe-ve - ril Thom-as A - qui-nas,and Doc-tor Sa-che-ve-rell

Fla-vour of Ham-let the Strang-er, a touch of him Lit-tle of Man-fred(but not ver - y much of him)

Tup-per and Ten - ny - son Dan - iel De - foe An - tho-ny Trol-lope and　Mis - ter Gui - zot!__

Bea-dle of Bur-ling-ton Rich-ard-son's show Mis-ter Mi-caw-ber and　Ma-dame Tus - saud!__

Ah! _____ Take of these el - e - ments

all that is fu - si - ble, Melt them all down in a pip-kin or cru - ci - ble, Set them to sim - mer and

take off the scum, ___ And a Heav - y Dra - goon is the re - sid - u -

1. um! _____ **2.** 2. If you um! _____

IF YOU'RE ANXIOUS FOR TO SHINE

Sung by Bunthorne

Words by
W. S. GILBERT

Music by
Sir ARTHUR SULLIVAN
BUNTHORNE

Allegretto grazioso

1. If you're anx-ious for to shine in the high aes-thet-ic line as a man of cul-ture rare, You must get up all the germs of the tran-scen-den-tal terms, and plant them ev-'ry-where. You must lie up-on the dais-ies and dis-

2. el-o-quent in praise of the ver-y dull old days which have long since passed a-way, And con-vince 'em, if you can that the reign of good Queen Anne was Cul-ture's palm-iest day. Of course you will pooh-pooh what-

3. sen-ti-men-tal pas-sion of a veg-e-ta-ble fash-ion must ex-cite your lan-guid spleen, An at-tach-ment à la Pla-to for a bash-ful young po-ta-to, or a not too-French French bean! Though the Phi-lis-tines may jos-tle, you will

Arr. by Hugo Frey

course in nov-el phras-es of your com-pli-cat-ed state of mind, The

ev-er's fresh and new, and de-clare it's crude and mean, For

rank as an a-pos-tle in the high aes-thet-ic band, If you

mean-ing does-n't mat-ter if it's on-ly i-dle chat-ter of a tran-scen-den-tal

Art stopped short in the cul-ti-vat-ed court of the Em-press Jo-seph-

walk down Pic-ca-dil-ly with a pop-py or a lil-ly in your me-di-ae-val

kind.

ine.

hand. And ev-'ry-one will

And ev-'ry-one will

And ev-'ry-one will

say, As you walk your mys-tic way, "If—

say, As you walk your mys-tic way, "If—

say, As you walk your flow'r-y way, "If—

this_ young man ex - press - es him - self in terms too deep for
that's not good e - nough_ for him which is good e - nough for
he's_ con - tent with a veg - e - ta - ble love which would cer - tain - ly not suit

me, Why, what a ver - y sin - gu - lar - ly deep young man this
me, Why, what a ver - y cul - ti - vat - ed kind of youth this
me, Why, what a most par - tic - u - lar - ly pure young man this

deep young man must be!"
kind of youth must be!"
pure young man must be!"

1.-2.   3.

2. Be___
3. Then a

fz

PRITHEE, PRETTY MAIDEN

Sung by Grosvenor and Patience

Words by
W. S. GILBERT

Music by
Sir ARTHUR SULLIVAN

Grosvenor: Prith-ee, pret-ty maid-en prith-ee, tell me true,
Patience: Gen-tle sir, my heart is frol-ic-some and free
Grosvenor: Prith-ee, pret-ty maid-en will you mar-ry me?
Patience: Gen-tle sir, al-though to mar-ry I de-sign

(Hey, but I'm dole-ful, wil-low wil-low wa-ly!) Have you e'er a lov-er a-
(Hey, but he's dole-ful, wil-low wil-low wa-ly!) No-bod-y I care for
(Hey, but I'm hope-ful, wil-low wil-low wa-ly!) I may say, at once, I'm a
(Hey, but he's hope-ful, wil-low wil-low wa-ly!) As yet I do not know you, and

dang-ling af-ter you? Hey wil-low wa-ly O! I would fain dis-cov-er
comes a-court-ing me Hey wil-low wa-ly O! No-bod-y I care for
man of prop-er-tee Hey wil-low wa-ly O! Mon-ey, I de-spise it;
so I must de-cline, Hey wil-low wa-ly O! To oth-er maid-ens go you As

If you have a lov-er! Hey__ wil-low wa-ly__ O!
Comes a-court-ing there-fore Hey__ wil-low wa-ly__ O!
Man-y peo-ple prize it, Hey__ wil-low wa-ly__ O!
yet I do not know you, Hey__ wil-low wa-ly__ O!

Arr. by Hugo Frey

"Patience"

SILVER'D IS THE RAVEN HAIR

Sung by Jane

Words by
W. S. GILBERT

Music by
Sir ARTHUR SULLIVAN

Andante moderato

1. Sil-vered is the ra-ven hair, Spread-ing is the part-ing straight, Mot-tled the com-plex-ion fair, Halt-ing is the youth-ful gait, Hol-low is the laugh-ter free, Spec-ta-cled the lim-pid eye Lit-tle will be

2. Fad-ing is the ta-per waist, Shape-less grows the shape-ly limb, And al-though se-vere-ly laced, Spread-ing is the fig-ure trim! Stout-er than I used to be, Still more cor-pu-lent grow I There will be too

Arr. by Hugo Frey

left— of— me In the com - ing bye and bye!
much— of— me In the com - ing bye and bye!

1.
Lit - tle will be left of me In the com - ing— bye and bye!—

2.
There will be too much of me In the com - ing— bye and bye!—

"Patience"

A Magnet Hung 'In A Hardware Shop

Sung by Grosvenor and Chorus

Words by
W. S. GILBERT

Music by
Sir ARTHUR SULLIVAN

GROSVENOR

Allegretto

mag - net hung in a hard-ware shop, And all a-round was a lov-ing crop Of
I - ron and Steel ex - pressed sur-prise, The nee-dles o - pened their well-drilled eyes, The

scis - sors and nee - dles,_ nails and knives, Of - fer - ing love for
pen - knives felt "shut_ up," no doubt, The scis - sors de - clared them-

all_ their_ lives; But for
selves "cut_ out," The

i - ron the mag - net felt no whim,
ket - tles they boiled with rage, 'tis said,

mf

Though he charm - ed i - ron, it charmed not him, From
While ev - 'ry nail went off it's head, And

p

nee - dles and nails and knives he'd turn, For he'd set his love ____
hith - er and thith - er be - gan to roam, Till a ham - mer came up ____

CHORUS   GROSVENOR

____ on a Sil - ver Churn!   A Sil - ver Churn?   A
____ and drove them home.   It drove them home?   It

LOVE IS A PLAINTIVE SONG

Sung by Patience

Words by
W. S. GILBERT

Music by
Sir ARTHUR SULLIVAN

1. Love is a plain-tive song, Sung by a suf-f'ring maid, Tell-ing a tale of wrong, Tell-ing of hope be-tray'd. Tun'd to each chang-ing note, Sor-ry when he is sad,
2. Ren-der-ing good for ill, Smil-ing at ev-'ry frown, Yield-ing your own self-will, Laugh-ing your tear-drops down, Nev-er a self-ish whim, Trou-ble or pain to stir,

Arr. by Hugo Frey

Blind to his ev - 'ry mote, Mer - ry when he ___ is
Ev - er - y - thing for him, Noth - ing at all ___ for

glad! Mer - ry when he ___ is glad! ___
her! Noth - ing at all ___ for her! ___

p a tempo

Love that no wrong can cure, Love that is al - ways new,
Love that will aye en - dure, Tho' the re wards be few,

That is the love that's pure, ___ That is the love ___ that's
That is the love that's pure, ___ That is the love ___ that's

WHEN I GO OUT OF DOOR

Sung by Bunthorne and Grosvenor

Words by
W. S. GILBERT

Music by
Sir ARTHUR SULLIVAN

Arr. by Hugo Frey

151

AFTER MUCH DEBATE INTERNAL

Finale
Sung by the Duke, Bunthorne and Chorus

Words by
W. S. GILBERT

Music by
Sir ARTHUR SULLIVAN

Af- ter much de-bate in-ter-nal, I on La-dy Jane de-cide, Sa-phir now may take the Col-onel, An-gy be the Ma-jor's bride! In that case un-pre-ce-dent-ed, Sin-gle I must live and die I shall

have to be con-tent-ed With a tu-lip or li-ly He will

have to be con-tent-ed With a tu-lip or li-ly!

In that

case un-pre-ce-dent-ed, Sin-gle he must live and die, He will

THE PIRATES OF PENZANCE

or THE SLAVE OF DUTY

First performed December 31, 1879, at the Fifth Avenue Theatre, New York

THE STORY

Frederic, the pirates' apprentice, has today finished his training and become a real pirate, and the pirates celebrate the occasion on Cornwall's rocky coast—but Frederic is unhappy.

Ruth, the pirates' maid-of-all-work, tells them why. She had been Frederic's nursery maid and, being half-deaf, when told by his father to apprentice him to a pilot, had understood the word to be pirate, and made him a pirate's apprentice instead.

Frederic's sense of duty forces him to leave them forever and to turn honest, and war against his pirate friends. He first begs them to give up piracy, but the Pirate King insists it is better far to live and die under the brave black flag. The pirates, being all orphans themselves, are tender-hearted toward orphans.

Ruth wants Frederic to marry her, and dreads his seeing younger girls. A bevy of maidens appear, and Frederic, charmed by their beauty, leaves Ruth. The girls are frightened by Frederic's admission that he is a pirate. He insists he is now reformed, but none of them will take pity on him till Mabel enters. She sings, "Poor Wandering One", and tells him "Take heart—take any heart, take mine."

The pirates enter stealthily, each seizing one of the girls. Mabel warns them all the girls are Wards in Chancery, and their father is a Major General. The Major General enters, and the pirates ask to marry the girls, his daughters. He objects to pirates as sons-in-law. Mabel says, "Frederic from today on is no pirate, but means to lead a blameless life."

The Major General tells the pirates he is an orphan, and as they are all orphans, and tender-hearted to others, they leave the girls. Frederic spurns Ruth and goes with the pirates.

The Major General is seated with his daughters and Mabel in a ruined chapel, when Frederic enters. The General confesses he is hiding from the pirates' revenge, as he told them he was an orphan, but isn't, as he has purchased a tomb of ancestors (now his).

Frederic announces his expedition will march against the pirates at eleven and by midnight he will have atoned for his pirate days by wiping them out, and then he can freely marry Mabel. His army of policemen enter, and the girls cheer them on. Frederic is about to leave with them, when the Pirate King and Ruth arrive, holding a pistol each to Frederic's ear. Ruth and the King explain that Frederic was born in a Leap Year, and so won't reach his twenty-first birthday until 1940. Legally, he is still the pirates' apprentice.

Frederic, as always, a slave of duty, joins the pirates again and dutifully tells them the General is not, after all, an orphan. Frederic abandons Mabel, promising to return to her in 1940. The police return and Mabel tells them Frederic has joined the pirates. The sergeant says, "The policeman's lot is not a happy one", but decides to capture the pirates.

The pirates are heard singing, advancing on the General. The police hide. The pirates enter. As they are about to kill the General, the Police attack them, but the pirates win and stand over them with drawn swords. The police appeal to the pirates to spare them, in Queen Victoria's name. The pirates spare their lives "because, with all our faults, we love our Queen."

The police arrest the pirates, but Ruth discloses the fact that the pirates are all "noblemen who have gone wrong". The General declares, "We love our House of Peers", and the pirates go free.

The General gives his daughters in marriage to the pirates. Mabel and Frederic are reunited.

"The Pirates of Penzance"

When Fred'ric Was A Little Lad

Sung by Ruth

Words by
W. S. GILBERT

Music by
Sir **ARTHUR SULLIVAN**

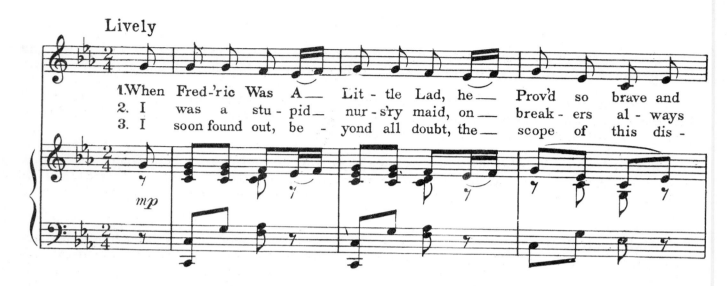

1. When Fred-'ric Was A__ Lit-tle Lad, he__ Prov'd so brave and
2. I was a stu-pid__ nur-s'ry maid, on__ break-ers al-ways
3. I soon found out, be-yond all doubt, the__ scope of this dis-

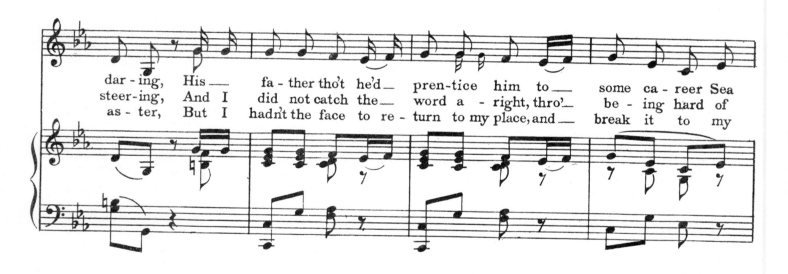

dar-ing, His__ fa-ther tho't he'd pren-tice him to__ some ca-reer Sea
steer-ing, And I did not catch the__ word a-right, thro'__ be-ing hard of
as-ter, But I hadn't the face to re-turn to my place, and__ break it to my

far-ing. I__ was a-las! his__ nur-s'ry maid, and__
hear-ing. Mis-tak-ing my in-struc-tions which with
mas-ter. A__ nur-s'ry maid is__ ne'er a-fraid of__

Arr. by Hugo Frey

"The Pirates of Penzance"

Oh, Better Far To Live And Die

Sung by the Pirate King

Words by
W. S. GILBERT

Music by
Sir ARTHUR SULLIVAN

Moderato

pi - rates all — are well - to - do, But I'll be true to the song I sing, And
wants to call — his crown his own, Must man - age some - how to get through More

live — and die a Pi - rate King;
dir - ty work than ev - er I do. } For — I am a Pi - rate

CHORUS
KING
King! You are! Hur - rah for our Pi - rate King! And it is, it is a

glor - i - ous thing — to be a Pi - rate King! ——— For I

CHORUS

KING

am a Pi - rate King! _____ And it
You are! Hur - rah for our Pi - rate King!

is, it is a glor - i - ous thing __ to be a Pi - rate

CHORUS

King! It is! Hur - rah for our Pi - rate King! Hur - rah for the

f

1.

Pi - rate King! _____ 2. When I

2.

King! _____

ff

Climbing Over Rocky Mountain

Sung by the Chorus

Words by
W. S. GILBERT

Music by
Sir **ARTHUR SULLIVAN**

Allegro grazioso

CHORUS

Climb-ing o - ver rock-y moun-tain, Skip-ping riv - u - let and foun-tain, Pass-ing where the wil - lows qui - ver,

Pass-ing where the wil-lows qui - ver By the ev - er - roll-ing riv- er, Swol-len with the summer rain, the sum - mer rain;

Thread-ing long and leaf-y maz-es Dot-ted with un -

cresc.

num-bered dai-sies, Dot-ted, dot-ted with un-num-bered dai sies;

Scal-ing rough and rug-ged pass-es, Climb the har-dy__ lit-tle las-sies, Till__ the__

bright sea - shore they gain; Scal-ing rough and__ rug-ged pass-es,

Climb the har-dy__ lit-tle las-sies, Till__ the__ bright sea - shore they gain.__

OH, IS THERE NOT ONE MAIDEN?

Sung by Frederic

Words by
W. S. GILBERT

Music by
Sir ARTHUR SULLIVAN

"The Pirates of Penzance"

POOR WAND'RING ONE

Sung by Mabel

Words by
W. S. GILBERT

Music by
Sir ARTHUR SULLIVAN

Arr. by Hugo Frey

"The Pirates of Penzance"

I AM THE VERY MODEL

Sung by Major-General and Chorus

Words by
W. S. GILBERT

Music by
Sir ARTHUR SULLIVAN

GENERAL

man - y cheer-ful facts a - bout the square of the hy - po-ten - use With
whis-tle all the airs from that in - fer - nal non - sense, Pin - a - fore! And

man - y cheer-ful facts a-bout the square of the hy - po-ten-use, With man-y cheer-ful facts a-bout the
whis-tle all the airs from that in - fer - nal non-sense, Pin-a-fore, And whis-tle all the airs from that in -

cresc.

square of the hy - po-ten-use, With man - y cheer-ful facts a-bout the square of the hy - po-ten-po-ten-
fer - nal non-sense, Pin-a-fore, And whis-tle all the airs from that in - fer-nal non-sense, Pin-a - pin-a -

cresc.

GENERAL

use.
fore.

I'm ver - y good at in - teg - ral and
Then I can write a wash-ing bill in

p

dif-fer-en-tial cal-cu-lus; I know the sci-en-tif-ic names of be-ings an-i-mal-cu-lous. In
Bab-y-lon-ic cu-nei-form, And tell you ev-'ry de-tail of Ca-rac-ta-cus-'s u-ni-form In

short, in mat-ters veg-e-ta-ble, an-i-mal, and min-er-al, } I am the ver-y mod-el of a
short, in mat-ters veg-e-ta-ble, an-i-mal, and min-er-al, }

CHORUS

mod-ern Ma-jor-Gin-er-al In short, in mat-ters veg-e-ta-ble, an-i-mal, and min-er-al, He

is the ver-y mod-el of a mod-ern Ma-jor-Gin-er-al.

"The Pirates of Penzance"

When The Foe-man Bares His Steel

Sung by Sergeant and Policemen

Words by
W. S. GILBERT

Music by
Sir ARTHUR SULLIVAN

"The Pirates of Penzance"

OH, LEAVE ME NOT TO PINE

Sung by Mabel and Frederic

Words by
W. S. GILBERT

Music by
Sir ARTHUR SULLIVAN

Mabel: Ah, leave me not to pine a-lone and
Fred: Ah, must I leave thee here In end-less

des-o-late; No fate seem'd fair as mine, No hap-pi-ness so great! And
night to dream, Where joy is dark and drear, And sor-row all su-preme! Where

na-ture,day by day, Has sung,— in ac-cents clear, This joy-ous round-e-
na-ture,day by day, Will sing,— in al-tered tone, This wea-ry round-e-

lay; "He loves thee he is here. Fal- la, la, la, Fal-
lay: "He loves thee he is gone. Fal- la, la, la, Fal-

Arr. by Hugo Frey

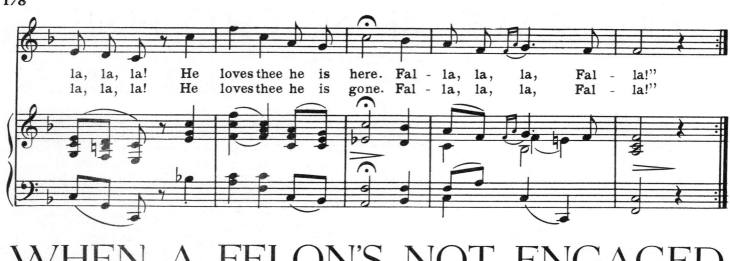

la, la, la! He loves thee he is here. Fal - la, la, la, Fal - la!"
la, la, la! He loves thee he is gone. Fal - la, la, la, Fal - la!"

WHEN A FELON'S NOT ENGAGED

Words by
W. S. GILBERT

Sung by Sergeant and Policemen

Music by
Sir ARTHUR SULLIVAN

1. When a fel-on's not en-gaged in his em-ploy-ment (his em-ploy-ment) Or ma-
2. en-ter-pris-ing bur-glar's not a - bur-gling (not a-burg-ling) When the

tur-ing his fe-lo-nious lit-tle plans (lit-tle plans) His ca-pa-ci-ty for in-no-cent en-
cut-throat is-n't oc-cu-pied in crime (-pied in crime) He loves to hear the lit-tle brook a-

joy-ment (cent en-joy-ment,) Is just as great as an-y hon-est man's (hon-est man's.) Our
gur-gling (brook a-gur-gling,) And lis-ten to the mer-ry vil-lage chime (vil-lage chime.) When the

Arr. by Hugo Frey

"The Pirates of Penzance"

WITH CATLIKE TREAD

Sung by Pirates and Policemen

Words by
W. S. GILBERT

Music by
Sir ARTHUR SULLIVAN

ly   the Pi - rate creeps, While all the house - hold sound - ly sleeps.

Come, friends, who plough the sea,   Truce to nav - i - ga - tion,

Take an - oth - er sta - tion, Let's va - ry pi - ra - cee   With a lit - tle bur - gla -

ree!   Come, friends, who plough the sea,   Truce to nav - i - ga - tion,

Take an-oth-er sta-tion; Let's va-ry pi-ra-cee,— With a lit-tle bur-gla-

ree! With cat-like tread Up-on our prey we steal;

In si-lence dread Our cau-tious way we feel.____

IOLANTHE

or THE PEER AND THE PERI

First performed November 25, 1882, at The Savoy, London

THE STORY

A group of fairies dance in, singing of the beauty of IOLANTHE, who was banished by the Fairy Queen 25 years before, for marrying a mortal. The penalty should have been death, but the Queen loved Iolanthe and now, at the fairies' urging, she pardons her. Iolanthe rises from the stream, where she has lived, to be nearer her son Strephon, an Arcadian shepherd. He is engaged to Phyllis. The marriage has been forbidden by her guardian, the Lord High Chancellor, but Strephon ignores that and sings joyfully to his mother, "I'm to be married today!"

After Iolanthe leaves, Phyllis joins Strephon and they sing of their marriage, though she reminds him he will get penal servitude for marrying a ward in chancery without her guardian's consent. They stroll away happily together, and the Peers enter, followed by the Lord High Chancellor, who tells them he loves Phyllis but since it is not seemly to marry his ward, he hopes she will choose one of themselves. He summons Phyllis, but she tells him she loves another. Strephon insists he will wed her, but the Chancellor separates them. Iolanthe, his mother, comforts him, but seeing him in Iolanthe's arms, Phyllis concludes he is faithless and, in jealous anger, becomes engaged to two of the Peers. The Fairy Queen pronounces a curse: She'll send Strephon to Parliament, where he will not only ennoble commoners, but also make the Peers sit throughout the grouse and salmon season!

The Fairy Queen falls in love with Private Willis, a sentry. Strephon, in parliament, passes at will bills which horrify the Peers. The Lord High Chancellor still loves Phyllis, and the Peers sing to him that "Faint heart ne'er won fair lady."

Strephon at length makes Phyllis realize that Iolanthe, though she looks seventeen, is really his mother, so Phyllis promises to wed him at once. The Lord Chancellor, not knowing this, decides that even though Phyllis is his ward, he will conquer his scruples over that and persuade her to marry him.

To prevent this, Iolanthe finally discloses to him the fact that she is his own long-lost wife. As she has broken her vow in telling him this, the Fairy Queen condemns her to death. But, at this, the fairies all admit that they have married the Peers. By Fairy law, they are all condemned to death also, for their law reads that "every fairy must die who marries a mortal".

But the Lord Chancellor says that "the subtleties of the legal mind are equal to the emergency", and he changes the law to read that "every fairy must die who does not marry a mortal".

The Fairy Queen, to save her own life, marries Private Willis, the sentry. Wings spread from the Peers' shoulders, and the whole company flies, singing, to Fairyland.

TRIPPING HITHER

Sung by Celia, Leila and Chorus

Words by
W. S. GILBERT

Music by
Sir ARTHUR SULLIVAN

Allegretto

We are dain-ty lit-tle fair-ies, Ev-er sing-ing, ev-er danc-ing,

We in-dulge in our va-ga-ries In a fash-ion most en-tranc-ing, _____ most en-

tranc - ing_____ most en - tranc - ing

Trip - ping hith - er, trip - ping

thith - er, No - bod - y knows why or whith - er.

"Iolanthe"

GOOD MORROW, GOOD LOVER!

Sung by Phyllis

Words by
W. S. GILBERT

Music by
Sir ARTHUR SULLIVAN

Arr. by Hugo Frey

"Iolanthe"

NONE SHALL PART US

Sung by Phyllis and Strephon

Words by
W. S. GILBERT

Music by
Sir ARTHUR SULLIVAN

Slowly, with expression

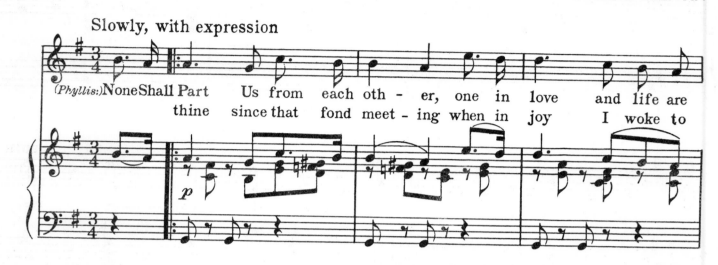

Arr. by Hugo Frey

MARCH OF THE PEERS

Words by
W. S. GILBERT

Music by
Sir ARTHUR SULLIVAN

Bow, bow, ye low-er mid-dle class-es! Bow, bow, ye trades-men, bow, ye mass-es, Blow the trum-pets, bang the brass-es, Tan-tan-ta-ra, Tzing, boom! Bow, bow, ye low-er mid-dle class-es, Bow, bow, ye trades-men, bow, ye mass-es, Blow the trum-pets,

bang_ the_ brass - es, Tan - tan - ta - ra! Tzing, boom, tzing, boom!

Tan - tan ta - ra! Tzing, boom, tzing, boom! Tan - tan - ta - ra! Tzing,

cresc.

boom, tzing, boom! Blow, blow the trum - pets, bang the brass - es!

Blow, blow the trum-pets, bang the brass-es!

Blow, blow the trum-pets, Blow, blow the trum-pets!

Tan-ta-ra, ta, ta ta ta ta ta, Tan-ta-ra, ta ta ta ta ta ta,

Tan-ta-ra, ta ta ta ta ta ta, Tan-ta-ra, ta ta ta ta ta ta,

Tan-ta-ra, ta ta, tan-ta-ra, ta ta, Tan-ta-ra, ta ta, tan-ta-ra, ta ta,

Tan-ta-ra, ta ta, Boom, tzing, boom!

Bow, ye low - er mid - dle class - es, Bow, ye

trades-men, bow, ye mass - es, Bow, ye low - er mid - dle class - es, Bow ye

trades-men, bow ye mass - es. Tan - tan - ta - ra tan - tan - ta -

ra, tan-ta-ra, tan-ta-ra, tan-ta-ra, tan-ta-ra, ra, ra, ra,

ra!   Tan-ta-ra!   Tan-ta-

ra!

The Law Is The True Embodiment

Sung by Lord Chancellor and Chorus of Peers

Words by
W. S. GILBERT

Music by
Sir ARTHUR SULLIVAN
LORD CHANCELLOR

Arr. by Hugo Frey

pret-ty young Wards in Chan - cer-y All ver-y a-gree-a-ble girls and none Are
quite pre-pared to mar-ry a-gain, But there'd be the deuce to pay in the Lords If I
one for you and one for ye And one for thou and one for thee But

o - ver the age of twen - ty - one. A
fell in love with one of my Wards! Which
nev - er, oh nev-er a one for me! Which

CHORUS

pleas-ant oc - cu - pa - tion for A rath - er sus-cep-ti-ble Chan-cel - lor! A
rath - er tries my tem-per, for I'm such a sus-cep-ti-ble Chan-cel - lor! Which
is ex - as - per - at - ing, for A high-ly sus-cep-ti-ble Chan-cel - lor! Which

1. - 2.   3.

pleas-ant oc - cu - pa - tion for A rath - er sus-cep-ti-ble Chan-cel-lor!
rath - er tries his tem-per, for He's such a sus-cep-ti-ble Chan-cel-lor!
is ex - as - per - at - ing, for A high-ly sus-cep-ti-ble

Chan-cel - lor!

"Iolanthe"

WHEN ALL NIGHT LONG

Sung by the Sentry

Words by
W. S. GILBERT

Music by
Sir ARTHUR SULLIVAN

SENTRY

1. When

all night long a chap re-mains On sen-try-go, to chase mo-not-o-ny He
in that House M. P.'s di-vide, If they've a brain and cer-e-bel-lum, too. They've

ex-er-cis-es of his brains, That is, as-sum-ing that he's got an-y. Tho'
got to leave that brain out-side, And vote just as their lead-ers tell 'em to. But

nev-er nur-tur'd in the lap Of lux-u-ry, Yet I ad-mon-ish you, I
then the pros-pect of a lot Of dull M. P.'s in close prox-im-i-ty, All

"Iolanthe"

OH, FOOLISH FAY

Sung by the Queen and Chorus

Words by
W. S. GILBERT

Music by
Sir ARTHUR SULLIVAN

Andante

QUEEN

1. Oh, fool-ish fay, Think you, be-cause His brave ar-
2. On fire that glows With heat in-tense I turn the

ray My bo-som thaws, I'd dis-o-bey Our fair-y
hose Of com-mon sense, And out it goes At small ex-

laws? Be-cause I fly In realms a-bove, In ten-den-
pense! We must main-tain Our fair-y law; That is the

soft as thine, Al - though I dare not
cold cas - cade Quench my great love I

say so! Oh, am -'rous dove!
won - der! Oh, Cap - tain Shaw!

CHORUS

Type of O - vid - ius Na - so! This heart of mine Is
Type of true love kept un - der! Could thy Bri - gade With

QUEEN

soft as thine, Al- though I dare not say so! ___
cold cas - cade Quench my great love I won der!

HE LOVES!

Sung by Iolanthe

Words by
W. S. GILBERT

Music by
Sir ARTHUR SULLIVAN

He loves! If in the by-gone years Thine eyes have ev-er shed Tears bit-ter, un-a-vail-ing tears For one un-time-ly dead If in the e-ven-tide of life Sad thoughts of her a-rise, Then let the mem-'ry of thy wife Plead for my boy he dies! He

"*Iolanthe*"

EV'RY ONE IS NOW A FAIRY

Finale
Sung by Phyllis, Lord Chancellor and Chorus

Words by
W. S. GILBERT

Music by
Sir ARTHUR SULLIVAN

Arr. by Hugo Frey

Ev - 'ry one is now a fair - y!
House of Peers for House of Pe - ris!

Lord Chan. Tho' as a gen - 'ral rule __ we know Two __ strings
Up in the air sky high, __ sky high, Free __ from

go to ev - 'ry bow, Make up your minds that
Wards in Chan - cer - y, I shall be sure - ly

grief 'twill bring, If you've two beaux to ev - 'ry string.
hap - pier, for I'm such a sus - cep - ti - ble Chan - cel - lor!

ALL

Though as a gen - 'ral rule— we know Two— strings
Up in the air, sky high,— sky high, Free— from

go to ev - 'ry bow, Make up your minds that grief 'twill
Wards in Chan - cer - y, He will be sure - ly hap - pier

bring, If you've two beaux to ev - 'ry string. 2. Up in the
for He's such a sus - cep - ti - ble

1.   LORD CHAN.

Chan - cel - lor!

2.

RUDDIGORE

or THE WITCH'S CURSE

First performed January 22, 1887, at The Savoy, London

THE STORY

Rose Maybud, a Village maiden, is wooed by all the lads, but her extreme beauty makes them too shy to ask her to wed, so, until she chooses one man, and marries, there is no chance for any other girl.

The Professional Bridesmaids, daily hours ten to four, since their services haven't been required for six months, are afraid of losing their jobs entirely, so, as a gentle hint, they serenade Rose Maybud.

Rose's Aunt Hannah, even is asked by the bridesmaids to marry and give them employment, but she tells them she is pledged to eternal maidenhood. She'd been engaged to a lad who'd wooed her under an assumed name. On her wedding day, she found him to be Sir Roderic Murgatroyd, of the Bad Baronets of Ruddigore, the uncle of the present Baronet. As one of the accursed line, Hannah spurned him, for he, like each Baronet of his family, was forced by the Witch's Curse to commit one crime a day or die in agony. Sir Roderic rebelled, and died ten years before this day.

Rose Maybud appears, studying a book of etiquette, her lifelong guide. Aunt Hannah asks Rose if she would be willing to marry Robin. Rose says only that he is shy, and hasn't asked her.

Robin Oakapple, the bashful young farmer, chances by. He speaks of love, but only impersonally, and she answers in the same way. After Rose leaves him, old Adam recognizes Robin as Sir Ruthven Murgatroyd in disguise.

Robin tells him he left the castle to escape the title, as he doesn't want to commit a crime a day. His brother Despard, thinking him dead, is now the Baronet, dutifully committing his crime a day.

Richard Dauntless, a bold, brave sailor, Robin's foster brother, comes home from the sea, after ten adventurous years. He promises Robin to woo Rose for him, as he is anything but bashful himself. But Richard falls in love with Rose, and tries to win her. Rose accepts Richard, but Robin is so truly noble about his loss that she transfers her promise to him.

Mad Margaret appears, weeping. Despard deserted her, as one of his daily crimes. She threatens to kill Rose, as she has a jealous fear that Despard may fall in love with her.

Sir Despard and his friends arrive at the moment of Rose's wedding. The girls flee from him in horror. Richard, in revenge, tells Despard the truth, that Robin is his older brother, thought dead, and is really the Baronet, and should have to do the daily crimes. Despard stops the wedding, and makes Robin accept the title, curse, daily crimes, and all. Rose feels it her duty to marry Despard, but he, now free of any compulsion, chooses Mad Margaret. Rose then tells Richard she'll marry him. He accepts.

In Ruddigore Castle, Robin, for his daily crime, when Richard and Rose come for his consent to their wedding, decides to abduct Rose, but Richard waves the Union Jack over her, and protects her, so Robin gives his consent. Robin is left alone. The ancestors, led by his Uncle Roderic, come alive, and step down from their picture frames. They berate Robin for not having committed a real crime as yet. They force him by torture to promise to abduct a lady—any lady.

Despard and Mad Margaret, married a week, are reformed characters. They urge Robin to reform, and despite the penalty of a painful death, he agrees. But Adam enters with the abducted girl— who turns out to be Rose's Aunt Hannah! Hannah attacks Robin with a dagger; Robin calls on his dead Uncle for help, and his Uncle steps from his picture frame to help him, recognizes Hannah as his lost love, and they embrace. Robin points out that his Uncle isn't dead, as refusal to commit the crime was suicide, and suicide is itself a crime. This also frees Robin who marries Rose.

IF SOMEBODY THERE CHANCED TO BE

Sung by Rose

Words by
W. S. GILBERT

Music by
Sir ARTHUR SULLIVAN

Arr. by Hugo Frey

says   of   those___ who___ point,   Their man - ners must   be
says   in   plain - est___ print,   "It's   most   un - la - dy-

out   of   joint.   You   may   not
like   to   hint.   You   may   not

point,   You   must   not   point,   It's   man - ners out   of
hint,   You   must   not   hint,   It   says   you must - n't

joint   to   point!   Ah! _____   Had
hint,   in   print!   Ah! _____   And

I KNOW A YOUTH

Sung by Rose and Robin

Words by
W. S. GILBERT

Music by
Sir ARTHUR SULLIVAN

I were the maid I would meet the lad half-way (For I real-ly do be-lieve that tim-id youth will— die!) Poor lit-tle man! Poor lit-tle maid! Poor lit-tle man! Poor lit-tle maid! I thank you, {sir, miss} for your coun-sel true; I'll tell that— {maid youth}——— what {she he} ought to do!

I SHIPP'D, D'YE SEE

Sung by Richard

Words by
W. S. GILBERT

Music by
Sir ARTHUR SULLIVAN

Hornpipe
8va ad lib.

When The Buds Are Blossoming

Sung by Rose and Chorus

Words by
W. S. GILBERT

Music by
Sir ARTHUR SULLIVAN

Arr. by Hugo Frey

When the buds are blos-som-ing, Smil-ing wel-come to the spring, Lov-ers choose a wed-ding day Life is love in mer-ry May, Life is love, life is love, in mer-ry May! Spring is green Fa la la la la la la la Sum-mer's

CHORUS

rose _____ Fa la la la la la la la la!

It ___ is sad when sum - mer

goes, Fa la _____ la la la la! Fa la! Fa la la la la

la la la! Fa la la la la la la la! Win - ter still is ___ far a -

way, far a - way Fa la la la la! Fa la la la la la Leaves in au - tumn

(TENOR)

fade and fall, Win-ter is the end of_ all. Fa la

la la la la la la,_

_ la la la la la la la la! Fa la____ la la la la la

la Fa la la la la la la la la la!

(Attacca)

Dance
L'istesso tempo

THE YEOMEN OF THE GUARD

or THE MERRYMAN AND HIS MAID

First performed October 3, 1888, at The Savoy, London

THE STORY

Colonel Fairfax, young and handsome soldier, is sentenced to death as a sorcerer. This grieves all the young maidens of Tower Green, but none more than Phoebe, Sergeant Meryll's daughter, who has fallen in love with the condemned man merely by watching him take his exercise on the prison walls.

Wilfred Shadbolt, Head Jailer and Assistant Tormentor, is jealous of the colonel and gloats over his impending doom. But Sergeant Meryll is a life-long friend of the colonel's, and forms a scheme to effect his escape. The plan is for the Colonel to change places with Leonard, Sergeant Meryll's son, who is a stranger to Tower Green, having just arrived as a new man of the Yeomen of the Guard. Phoebe's part in the scheme is to wheedle the keys from Wilfred, so that a uniform may be smuggled into the colonel's cell.

In the meantime, Fairfax arranges a hasty marriage to foil his kinsman, Sir Clarence Poltwhistle, who has charged the Colonel with sorcery in order to inherit his share of the estate. But Sir Clarence can inherit the estate only if the Colonel dies unmarried. So Sir Richard Cholmondeley, Lieutenant of the Tower, as a favor to Fairfax, finds Elsie Maynard, a strolling singer who, thinking she will be a widow in an hour anyway, agrees for a hundred pounds, which she needs to save her sick mother, to marry the Colonel. The marriage is performed. But Elsie, to her dismay, is left with a husband, for Sergeant Meryll's scheme works and the prisoner escapes. Even more dismayed is Jack Point, a jester, who has been Elsie's fellow performer, and who is in love with her.

Colonel Fairfax, masquerading as Leonard Meryll, wanders about Tower Green disguised as a Yeoman. Meeting Elsie, he falls in love with her, and finding out she is really his wife, woos her. Though in love with him, Elsie will not admit it, for she feels bound by her marriage to the escaped prisoner. And she, of course, does not recognize Colonel Fairfax as her husband, for she was masked during the ceremony.

Jack Point and Wilfred concoct a plot to convince Elsie she is a widow. Each thinks this will be to his advantage. Jack wants Elsie free so he can resume his suit. Wilfred, who has been condemned for allowing the prisoner to escape, thinks he can save his own life by pretending he has found and shot the Colonel. The absence of a corpus delicti he explains by saying the body sank in the river.

So Wilfred, with Jack Point serving as witness, dramatically announces the death of Colonel Fairfax. Elsie, believing herself free from the marriage, returns the very much alive Colonel's love. Phoebe, jealous, indiscreetly allows Wilfred to discover the false Yeoman's true identity, and to stop Wilfred's tongue, she agrees to marry him.

News arrives that the Colonel has been reprieved. Therefore, the false Yeoman reveals his true identity and claims Elsie as his bride.

But Dame Carruthers, who has been sighing after Sergeant Meryll, now sees her opportunity. Seeing that Colonel Fairfax could not have masqueraded as Leonard Meryll without the Sergeant's complicity, she threatens to expose him and, to buy her silence, he is forced to marry her.

WHEN A MAIDEN LOVES

Sung by Phoebe

Words by
W. S. GILBERT

Music by
Sir ARTHUR SULLIVAN

Arr. by Hugo Frey

"The Yeomen Of The Guard"

When Our Gallant Norman Foes

Sung by Dame Carruthers and Yeomen

Words by
W. S. GILBERT

Music by
Sir ARTHUR SULLIVAN

Allegro moderato maestoso

1. When our
2. With -

gal-lant Nor-man foes Made our mer - ry land their own, And the Sax-ons from the Con-quer - or were
in its wall of rock The flow-er of the brave Have per-ished with a con-stan-cy un-

fly - ing, At his bid-ding it a - rose, In its pan-o-ply of stone, A
shak - en. From the dun-geon to the block, From the scaf-fold to the grave, Is a

sen - ti-nel un-liv-ing and un-dy-ing. In sen-si-ble, I trow, As a
jour-ney man-y gal-lant hearts have tak-en. And the wick-ed flames may hiss Round the

Arr. by Hugo Frey

sen - ti - nel should be, Tho' a queen to save her head should come a - su - ing; There's a
he - roes who have fought For con-science and for home in all its beau - ty; But the

le - gend on its brow That is el - o-quent to me, And it tells of du - ty—
grim old fort - a-lice Takes lit - tle heed of aught That comes not in— the—

done— and du - ty do - ing. "The screw may twist and the
mea - sure of its du - ty.

rack— may turn, And men may bleed and men— may burn, O'er

Lon - don town and its gold - en hoard I keep my si - lent

CHORUS

watch and ward!" The screw may twist and the rack may turn, And men may bleed and

men may burn, O'er Lon - don town and its gold - en hoard I keep my

si - lent watch and ward! ward!

IS LIFE A BOON?

Sung by Colonel Fairfax

Words by
W. S. GILBERT

Music by
Sir ARTHUR SULLIVAN

Andante espressivo

1. Is life a boon? If so, it must be a fall That Death, when-e'er he call, Must call too soon. Though four - score years he give, Yet one would pray to live An - oth - er moon! What kind of plaint have I, Who per - ish in Ju -

2. Is life a thorn? Then count it not a whit! Nay, count it not a whit! Man is well done with it; Soon as he's born He should all means es - say To put the plague a - way; And I, war - worn, Poor cap - tured fu - gi -

ly, Who per - ish in Ju - ly? I might have had to
tive, My life most glad - ly give I might have had to

die, Per - chance, in June! I might have had to
live An - oth - er morn! I might have had to

1. die, Per - chance, in June! **2.** live, to live An - oth - er

morn!

WERE I THY BRIDE

Sung by Phoebe

Words by
W. S. GILBERT

Music by
Sir ARTHUR SULLIVAN

Were I thy bride, Then all the world be-side Were not too wide To hold my wealth of love ____ Were I thy bride! Up-on thy breast My lov-ing head would rest, As on her nest The ten-der tur-tle dove ____ Were I thy

bride! _____ This heart of mine Would be one heart with

thine, And in that shrine Our hap-pi-ness would dwell ____ Were I thy

bride! _____ And all day long Our lives should be a

song: No grief, no wrong Should make my heart re-bel ___ Were I thy bride! ____

The sil - v'ry flute, The mel - an - chol - y lute, Were night owl's hoot To my low - whis-pered coo Were I thy bride! _____

The sky - lark's trill Were but dis-cor-dance shrill To the soft thrill Of woo - ing as I'd woo Were

STRANGE ADVENTURE

Sung by Kate, Dame Carruthers, Fairfax and Sergeant Meryll

Words by
W. S. GILBERT

Music by
Sir ARTHUR SULLIVAN

Allegretto Tempo di Gavotte

1. Strange ad - ven - ture! Maid - en wed - ded To a _ groom she'd nev - er _
2. Strange ad - ven - ture that we're troll - ing: Mod - est _ maid and _ gal - lant _

seen! _____ Groom a - bout to be be - head - ed, In an _
groom! _____ While the fun - 'ral bell is toll - ing, Toll - ing, -

hour on Tow - er Green! _____ Groom in drear - y dun - geon
toll - ing, Bim - a - boom! Tow-er, Tow-er, Tow-er Green! Mod - est maid - en _ will not
                            Bim-a, Bim-a, Bim-a - boom!

Arr. by Hugo Frey

Copyright 1942 **ROBBINS MUSIC CORPORATION,**   New York, N. Y.
International Copyright Secured   Made in U. S. A.

TRIAL BY JURY

First performed March 25, 1875, at the Royalty Theatre, London

THE STORY

Angelina is suing Edwin for breach of promise. The Usher instructs the Jury:
> "With stern judicial frame of mind
> From bias free of every kind,
> This trial must be tried."

He tells them:
> "When amid the plaintiff's shrieks,
> The ruffianly defendant speaks—
> What he may say you needn't mind—"

The Jurymen shake their fists at Edwin when he tries to explain that he no longer loves Angelina, having fallen in love with another lady.

The Judge tells the story of his life: "When I, Good Friends, Was Called to the Bar", and explains how he came to be such a good judge. His rise is due to the fact that he married a "rich attorney's elderly, ugly daughter", and threw her over, when he had become successful.

When the procession of bridesmaids enters, the Judge takes a great fancy to the first Bridesmaid, and sends her a note by the Usher, which she reads, kisses rapturously, and places in her bosom. Then Angelina, the would-be bride, the "broken flower" enters, and at sight of her beauty, the Judge promptly transfers his affection to her. He directs the Usher to take the note from the First Bridesmaid, and hand it to Angelina, which the Usher does. Angelina reads it, kisses it rapturously, and places it in her bosom.

Her counsel sings:
> "See my interesting client,
> Victim of a heartless wile!
> See the traitor all defiant
> Wear a supercilious smile!"

He tells of Edwin deserting her,
> "Doubly criminal to do so,
> For the maid had bought her trousseau!"

Angelina is so affected herself by her counsel's eloquent plea for her, that she falls, weeping, in the arms of the Foreman of the Jury, and later, in the arms of the Judge. Though the Usher calls for silence in the court, the Jurors rage against Edwin, and insist he pay very great damages.

Edwin begs them not to be so hard on him for his fickleness, and promises:
> "I'll marry this lady today,
> And marry that lady tomorrow".

The Judge admits that this seems reasonable. But the Counsel says:
> "To marry two at once is Burglaree!"

The dilemma seems unsolvable, till the Judge impatiently declares, "I can't stop here all day!" and sings:
> "Put your briefs upon the shelf;
> I will marry her myself!"

As he embraces Angelina, he sings:
> "Of Beauty I'm a Judge,"

and all answer:
> "And a good Judge, too!"

I LOVE HIM, I LOVE HIM

Sung by Angelina and Edwin

Words by
W. S. GILBERT

Music by
Sir ARTHUR SULLIVAN

Arr. by Hugo Frey

thrash her, per-haps _____ I should kick her, I

Love _____ Him, I Love Him with fer - vour in -

BOTH.

creas - ing { I love him I wor - ship and mad - ly a -
{ A bul - ly, a ruf - fian, a bul - ly, a

dore, I love him, I wor - ship and mad - ly a - dore! _____
sot, a ruf - fian, a ruf - fian, a bul - ly, a sot! _____

OH, GENTLEMEN, LISTEN

Sung by Edwin

Words by
W. S. GILBERT

Music by
Sir ARTHUR SULLIVAN

THE SORCERER

First performed November 17, 1877, at the Opéra Comique, London

THE STORY

Alexis has a theory that people should not marry according to wealth or rank. He wants the villagers and the gentry alike to fall in love and marry with no thought of class distinctions. So he decides to buy a love-at-first-sight philter, and put it in the tea at the Village picnic. He begs his fiancee, Aline, to drink of it also, as he will, so that their love will be eternal. She tries to dissuade him from the whole idea, but finally promises.

Alexis calls in Mr. Wells, a respectable sorcerer, and buys the love-potion, which is put in the teapot. All drink, villagers and nobility. The spell works.

Alexis Pointdextre's fiancee, Aline Sangazure, is well-descended, and Alexis himself is a member of the Grenadier Guards. His father, Sir Marmaduke, had, in youth been in love with Aline's mother, Lady Sangazure. Constance Partlet, a village maiden, is in love with Dr. Daly, the Vicar, while Constance's mother is in love with the Notary.

But, after partaking of the love-potion, to their own bewilderment, all the village falls madly in love, but each with the wrong person. Sir Marmaduke himself falls in love with Mrs. Partlet. Aline's aristocratic mother falls in love with the Sorcerer, Mr. Wells, who is an engaged man. Poor Constance, who'd loved the Vicar, Dr. Daly, now falls desperately in love with the Notary, aged 67.

Worst of all, Aline, who'd only drunk the drugged tea, because Alexis wished it, falls out of love with Alexis, and deeply in love with Dr. Daly. Alexis is amazed at her perfidy. As she embraces Dr. Daly, Alexis starts to utter a lover's curse against her.

The Sorcerer halts him by telling him that there is one way, and one only, to undo the spell—he himself, or Alexis must die, must, in fact, give up his life to the powers of evil. Mr. Wells confesses frankly he'd rather it would be Alexis than himself. But the others decide that the Sorcerer is the person to die, so he politely assents, and sinks through a trap amid red fire.

The Vicar, Dr. Daly, returns Constance's love; Mrs. Partlet wins the Notary. Alexis' father, Sir Marmaduke, and Aline's mother, become engaged. Aline and Alexis are joyfully re-united. All go to Sir Marmaduke's estate for another banquet—without drugged tea.

WHEN HE IS HERE

Sung by Constance

Words by
W. S. GILBERT

Music by
Sir ARTHUR SULLIVAN

Slowly with feeling

When He Is Here, I sigh with plea - sure, When he is
joice, he shows no plea - sure, When I am

gone, I sigh with grief; My hope-less fear no soul can mea - sure, His
sad, it grieves him not; His sol - emn voice has tones I trea - sure, My

love a - lone can give my ach-ing heart re - lief, Can give my ach-ing heart re-
heart is glad, they so - lace my un-hap-py lot! They so - lace my un-hap - py

lief! When he is cold, I weep for sor - row, when he is
lot! When I de - spond, my woe they chas - ten, when I take

Arr. by Hugo Frey

kind,   I weep for joy.   My grief un - told knows no to - mor - row, my
heart,   My hope they cheer,   With fol - ly fond to him I has - ten, with

grief un - told knows no to - mor - row;   My woe can find no hope, no
fol - ly fond to him I has - ten;   From him a - part, my life is

so - lace, no al - loy! No hope, no hope, no so - lace, no al -
ver - y sad and drear! My life, my life is ver - y sad and

loy! When I re - drear!

IT IS NOT LOVE

Ballad

Words by
W. S. GILBERT

Music by
Sir ARTHUR SULLIVAN

1. Thou hast the pow'r thy vaunt-ed love To sanc-ti-fy, all doubt a-bove, De-spite the gath-'ring shade; To make that love of thine so sure That, come what may, it

2. Thine is the pow'r, and thine a-lone, To place me on so proud a throne That kings might en-vy me! A price-less throne of love un-told, More rare than o-rient

Arr. by Hugo Frey

PRINCESS IDA

or CASTLE ADAMANT

First performed January 5, 1884, at The Savoy, London

THE STORY

On a pavilion of the palace, King Hildebrand, his son Prince Hilarion, and their soldiers and courtiers await Princess Ida and her father, King Gama.

Princess Ida, when a year old, was engaged to Prince Hilarion. The Prince wonders now what twenty years have done to his baby bride.

To Hilarion's disappointment, Ida's father, King Gama, arrives without her. He explains that Princess Ida now rules a woman's university. There, in its sacred precincts, she and her lovely pupils have forsworn wicked men. Marriage is forbidden.

Prince Hilarion, with some of his boon companions, go to storm Princess Ida's university, which is called Castle Adamant. They chain Gama up and leave him as hostage. Hilarion, Cyril and Florian climb over the wall and steal into the college, disguising themselves in girls' graduation gowns.

Ida enters, reading. Prince Hilarion greets her, and says that he and two other girls are desirous of entering her university as students. She accepts them. But one of Ida's students, Psyche, is Florian's sister and recognizes him. He tells her that Prince Hilarion is the man to whom Princess Ida is still engaged. Melissa overhears and likes the men but, unfortunately, her mother guesses that they are men. Hilarion, in his role as a woman, tells Ida that Prince Hilarion longs for her at his court.

Cyril, tipsy, sings a love song, which causes the three men to be discovered. In the resulting chaotic rush to evict the three men, Princess Ida falls into the stream and Hilarion rescues her.

Ida has the men arrested, and taken away in chains.

King Hildebrand and his soldiers break in the gates to the castle, and he threatens to level her halls. Ida defies him, and decides to defend her citadel. The ladies arm themselves with battle-axes. They leave the rifles in their armory, for fear they might go off. Finally, they rebel at fighting men so Princess Ida declares she will fight alone.

Ida's father and brothers come to fight to protect her. Since her women deserted her, she accepts them. But her father is still a slave of King Hildebrand, and must return to captivity. He says his sons may fight for her. She agrees to the plan that her three brothers shall fight Hilarion and his two friends.

Prince Hilarion and his two friends win. Ida bids her ladies bind up her brothers' wounds—but looks the other way.

Hildebrand tells Ida, "Women deserted you—try man". Ida's father asks her if her mother had hated man, where would Ida herself be now? Ida has no answer for that. She yields, and marries Prince Hilarion.

OH, GODDESS WISE

Sung by Princess

Words by
W. S. GILBERT

Music by
Sir ARTHUR SULLIVAN

Oh, god-dess wise That lov-est light, En-dow with sight Their un-il-lu-min'd eyes. At this my call, A fer-vent few Have come to woo The rays that from thee fall,_____ that from thee fall. Oh, god-dess wise That lov-est_ light, That lov-est light_____ Let fer-vent

Andante espressivo

rall.

a tempo

Arr. by Hugo Frey

words and fer - vent thoughts be mine, _____ That I may _ lead them to thy sa - cred shrine! Let fer - vent words and fer - vent thoughts be mine, That I _____ may lead them to thy sa - cred shrine I _ may lead them to thy sacred shrine, thy sa - cred shrine! _____

Merrily Ring The Luncheon Bell!

Sung by Blanche, Cyril and Chorus

Words by
W. S. GILBERT

Music by
Sir ARTHUR SULLIVAN

BLANCHE

Hun - ger, I beg to state, Is high - ly in - del - i - cate, This is a fact pro-found-ly true,

CHORUS

So learn your ap-pe-tites to sub-due. Yes, yes, We'll learn our

ap-pe-tites to sub - due!

CYRIL

Ma - dam, your words so wise, No - bod - y should de-spise,

Curs'd with an ap-pe-tite keen I am, And I'll sub - due it